THE GREATEST PAGES OF
CHARLES DICKENS

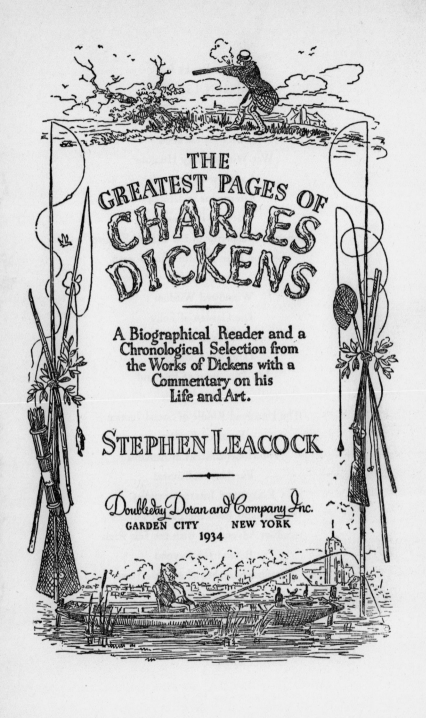

THE
GREATEST PAGES OF
CHARLES
DICKENS

A Biographical Reader and a
Chronological Selection from
the Works of Dickens with a
Commentary on his
Life and Art.

STEPHEN LEACOCK

Doubleday Doran and Company Inc.
GARDEN CITY   NEW YORK
1934

PRINTED AT THE *Country Life Press*, GARDEN CITY, N. Y., U. S. A.

Preface

WITH THE PASSAGE OF YEARS *almost all personal recollection of Charles Dickens is gone. Even remembrance at one remove grows dim. Already the great age in which he lived is passing into retrospect. The popularity of Dickens's works loses but little with the lapse of time. But many readers now come to them without that knowledge of the life of Dickens and the environment in which he lived which alone gives to his books their fullest significance.*

The aim of the present volume is to reproduce some of the most notable pages of Dickens's work in connection with the facts of his personal history and the development of his art. Of the selections here presented, most are chosen for their literary excellence as masterpieces of English literature. Others are included, not for their special artistic merit but for their significance in Dickens's life; such, for example, is the first story in which he saw himself in print, his eyes dim with tears of pride and joy; and those closing paragraphs which his tired hand traced upon the paper amid the glories of an afternoon in June—his last. So, too, the American extracts recall to us upon this continent not only Dickens's life history but our own.

It is hoped that such a work may be of service not only to readers of fiction, but also to those who approach the work of Dickens as students of literature and disciples of a master.

STEPHEN LEACOCK

McGill University,
May 1, 1934

Contents

Contents

Halftone Illustrations

Text Illustrations

CHILDHOOD AND YOUTH OF DICKENS
1812–1836

Chapter One

CHILDHOOD AND YOUTH OF DICKENS
1812–1836

CHARLES DICKENS was born in a suburb of Portsmouth, England, on February 7, 1812. His father, John Dickens, whom he afterwards immortalized as Mr. Micawber, was a clerk in the Navy Pay Office, with a falling salary and a rising family; a shiftless, cheery sort of man, always in and out of debt, with a queer grandiloquence in his speech and a mirage of illusion before his eyes. Dickens's mother—garrulous, illogical, and impossible—was known later to the world as Mrs. Nickleby.

John Dickens was moved by the Admiralty to Chatham, where little Charles had some casual schooling (1816–1821); and from there to London, where the family lived in one shabby-genteel home after another. Presently, the war being well over, John Dickens was paid off on a minute pension and subsided in due course into the debtors' prison of the Marshalsea (1822). The fortunes of his little son, now ten years old, here reached their lowest point. He became a sort of working drudge in a tumble-down factory, sleeping in an attic room, with the prison as his Sunday home. Here sat his father, mingling his tears and his optimism over a pint of porter.

A favouring shift of the wind of fortune carried John Dickens out of prison. The family moved into a respectable house. Young Charles went to a real school. His father, by an odd transformation, became a reporter in the gallery of the House of Commons. Charles Dickens presently became a clerk—not articled, in fact a sort of office boy—with a legal firm. He set to work to educate himself, read in the British Museum, and attended with passionate absorption innumerable performances of London melodrama. He fell head over heels in love—as did David Copperfield with Dora, but his idol was torn from him by parents a cut above his lot. He consoled his broken heart by learning shorthand and got a post (1829) as a reporter in odd, old-fashioned law courts called "Doctors Commons." Here he acquired that ripe knowledge of procedure in regard to marriage, to licenses, to legacies and so forth, which he afterwards implanted in Mr. Weller senior and others of his creations. From Doctors Commons Dickens rose to a seat beside his father in the parliamentary gallery. Here he became inspired with the abiding sense of the comic and amusing nature of British government which never left him.

But his own thoughts turned not to politics but to the stage and to letters. Only an odd chance prevented

CHARLES DICKENS as DAVID COPPERFIELD

(From an etching by "Phiz")

him from becoming an actor. But writing stories—
or making them up in his head—had been his predilection since his earliest childhood. Now at last he wrote
one down in earnest and sent it to a periodical (the
Old Monthly Magazine).

In due course he saw himself in all the majesty of
print. "On which occasion," so he himself has told us,
"I walked down to Westminster Hall and turned into
it for half an hour, because my eyes were so dimmed
with joy and pride that they could not bear the street
and were not fit to be seen there."

With this, Charles Dickens was launched upon the
world as a writer, the stage fading into the background.
The story that he wrote was called *A Dinner at Poplar
Walk*. When it and others were gathered together as
the *Sketches by Boz* the name was altered to *Mr. Minns
and His Cousin*. "Boz" was a family nickname broken
down from Moses. It took Dickens years to live it down.

One notes the basis of the humour of these sketches
as the mere fun of discomfiture and misadventure, the
stock in trade of the comic writers of the day. But
Dickens was soon to rise to a higher plane and a newer
art. He began where the others left off. But the little
story, like its fellows that rapidly followed it, has more
in it than the mere comic element. The power of vivid
description, a main feature of Dickens's craftsmanship,
is already apparent.

A DINNER AT POPLAR WALK

(Sketches by boz: *title changed later to* mr. minns AND HIS COUSIN)

Mr. Augustus Minns was a bachelor, of about forty as he said—of about eight-and-forty as his friends said. He was always exceedingly clean, precise, and tidy; perhaps somewhat priggish, and the most retiring man in the world. He usually wore a brown frock-coat without a wrinkle, light inexplicables without a spot, a neat neckerchief with a remarkably neat tie, and boots without a fault; moreover, he always carried a brown silk umbrella with an ivory handle. He was a clerk in Somerset House, or, as he said himself, he held "a responsible situation under Government." He had a good and increasing salary, in addition to some £10,000 of his own (invested in the funds), and he occupied a first floor in Tavistock Street, Covent Garden, where he had resided for twenty years, having been in the habit of quarrelling with his landlord the whole time; regularly giving notice of his intention to quit on the first day of every quarter, and as regularly countermanding it on the second. There were two classes of created objects which he held in the deepest and most unmingled horror—these were dogs and children. He was not unamiable, but he could, at any time, have viewed the execution of a dog, or the assassination of an infant,

8

with the liveliest satisfaction. Their habits were at
variance with his love of order; and his love of order
was as powerful as his love of life. Mr. Augustus Minns
had no relations, in or near London, with the exception
of his cousin, Mr. Octavius Budden, to whose son,
whom he had never seen (for he disliked the father),
he had consented to become godfather by proxy. Mr.
Budden, having realised a moderate fortune by ex-
ercising the trade or calling of a corn-chandler, and
having a great predilection for the country, had pur-
chased a cottage in the vicinity of Stamford Hill,
whither he retired with the wife of his bosom, and his
only son, Master Alexander Augustus Budden. One
evening as Mr. and Mrs. B. were admiring their son,
discussing his various merits, talking over his education, and disputing whether the classics should be
made an essential part thereof, the lady pressed so
strongly upon her husband the propriety of cultivating
the friendship of Mr. Minns in behalf of their son,
that Mr. Budden at last made up his mind that it
should not be his fault if he and his cousin were not
in future more intimate.

"I'll break the ice, my love," said Mr. Budden,
stirring up the sugar at the bottom of his glass of
brandy-and-water, and casting a sidelong look at his
spouse to see the effect of the announcement of his
determination, "by asking Minns down to dine with
us on Sunday."

"Then pray, Budden, write to your cousin at once,"

replied Mrs. Budden. "Who knows, if we could only get him down here, but he might take a fancy to our Alexander, and leave him his property?—Alick, my dear, take your legs off the rail of the chair!"

"Very true," said Mr. Budden, musing, "very true, indeed, my love!"

On the following morning, as Mr. Minns was sitting at his breakfast-table, alternately biting his dry toast, and casting a look upon the columns of his morning paper, which he always read from the title to the printer's name, he heard a loud knock at the street-door; which was shortly afterwards followed by the entrance of a servant, who put into his hand a particularly small card, on which was engraven, in immense letters, "Mr. Octavius Budden, Amelia Cottage (Mrs. B.'s name was Amelia), Poplar Walk, Stamford Hill."

"Budden!" ejaculated Minns; "what can bring that vulgar man here! Say I'm asleep—say I'm out, and shall never be home again—anything to keep him down-stairs."

"But please, sir, the gentleman's coming up," replied the servant: and the fact was made evident by an appalling creaking of boots on the staircase, accompanied by a pattering noise; the cause of which Minns could not, for the life of him, divine.

"Hem!—show the gentleman in," said the unfortunate bachelor. Exit servant, and enter Octavius, preceded by a large white dog, dressed in a suit of fleecy hosiery, with pink eyes, large ears, and no perceptible tail.

The cause of the pattering on the stairs was but too plain. Mr. Augustus Minns staggered beneath the shock of the dog's appearance.

"My dear fellow, how are you?" said Budden, as he entered.

He always spoke at the top of his voice, and always said the same thing half a dozen times.

"How are you, my hearty?"

"How do you do, Mr. Budden? Pray take a chair!" politely stammered the discomfited Minns.

"Thank you—thank you—well—how are you, eh?"

"Uncommonly well, thank you," said Minns, casting a diabolical look at the dog, who, with his hind-legs on the floor, and his fore-paws resting on the table, was dragging a bit of bread-and-butter out of a plate preparatory to devouring it, with the buttered side next the carpet.

"Ah, you rogue!" said Budden to his dog; "you see, Minns, he's like me, always at home, eh, my boy?— Egad, I'm precious hot and hungry! I've walked all the way from Stamford Hill this morning."

"Have you breakfasted?" inquired Minns.

"Oh, no!—came to breakfast with you; so ring the bell, my dear fellow, will you? and let's have another cup and saucer, and the cold ham. Make myself at home, you see!" continued Budden, dusting his boots with a table-napkin. "Ha!—ha!—ha!—'pon my life, I'm hungry."

Minns rang the bell, and tried to smile.

"I decidedly never was so hot in my life," continued

Octavius, wiping his forehead. "Well, but how are you, Minns? 'Pon my soul, you wear capitally."

"D'ye think so?" said Minns; and he tried another smile.

"'Pon my life, I do!"

"Mrs. B. and—what's his name—quite well?"

"Alick—my son, you mean; never better—never better. But at such a place as we've got at Poplar Walk, you know, he couldn't be ill if he tried. When I first saw it, by Jove! it looked so knowing, with the front garden, and the green railings, and the brass knocker, and all that—I really thought it was a cut above me."

"Don't you think you'd like the ham better," interrupted Minns, "if you cut it the other way?" He saw, with feelings which it is impossible to describe, that his visitor was cutting, or rather maiming, the ham in utter violation of all established rules.

"No, thank ye," returned Budden, with the most barbarous indifference to crime. "I prefer it this way —it eats short. But I say, Minns, when will you come down and see us? You will be delighted with the place; I know you will. Amelia and I were talking about you the other night, and Amelia said—another lump of sugar, please; thank ye—she said, don't you think you could contrive, my dear, to say to Mr. Minns, in a friendly way—come down, sir—damn the dog! he's spoiling your curtains, Minns—ha!—ha!—ha!" Minns leaped from his seat as though he had received the discharge from a galvanic battery.

"Come out, sir!—go out, hoo!" cried poor Augustus, keeping, nevertheless, at a very respectful distance from the dog; having read of a case of hydrophobia in the paper of that morning. By dint of great exertion, much shouting, and a marvellous deal of poking under the tables with a stick and umbrella, the dog was at last dislodged, and placed on the landing outside the door, where he immediately commenced a most appalling howling; at the same time vehemently scratching the paint off the two nicely-varnished bottom panels, until they resembled the interior of a backgammon board.

"A good dog for the country that!" coolly observed Budden to the distracted Minns, "but he's not much used to confinement. But now, Minns, when will you come down? I'll take no denial, positively. Let's see, to-day's Thursday. Will you come on Sunday? We dine at five—don't say no—do."

After a great deal of pressing, Mr. Augustus Minns, driven to despair, accepted the invitation, and promised to be at Poplar Walk on the ensuing Sunday at a quarter before five to the minute.

"Now mind the direction," said Budden; "the coach goes from the Flower-pot, in Bishopsgate Street, every half-hour. When the coach stops at the Swan, you'll see, immediately opposite you, a white house."

"Which is your house—I understand," said Minns, wishing to cut short the visit, and the story, at the same time.

"No, no, that's not mine; that's Grogus's, the great

ironmonger's. I was going to say—you turn down by
the side of the white house till you can't go another step
further—mind that!—and then you turn to your right,
by some stables—well, close to you, you'll see a wall
with 'Beware of the Dog' written on it in large letters
—(Minns shuddered)—go along by the side of that wall
for about a quarter of a mile—and anybody will show
you which is my place."

"Very well—thank ye—good-bye."

"Be punctual."

"Certainly; good morning."

"I say, Minns, you've got a card."

"Yes, I have; thank ye." And Mr. Octavius Budden
departed, leaving his cousin looking forward to his visit
of the following Sunday with the feelings of a penniless
poet to the weekly visit of his Scotch landlady.

Sunday arrived; the sky was bright and clear; crowds
of people were hurrying along the streets, intent on their
different schemes of pleasure for the day; everything
and everybody looked cheerful and happy except Mr.
Augustus Minns.

The day was fine, but the heat was considerable.
When Mr. Minns had fagged up the shady side of Fleet
Street, Cheapside, and Threadneedle Street, he had become pretty warm, tolerably dusty, and it was getting
late into the bargain. By the most extraordinary good
fortune, however, a coach was waiting at the Flower-
pot, into which Mr. Augustus Minns got, on the
solemn assurance of the cad that the vehicle would start

in three minutes—that being the very utmost extremity of time it was allowed to wait by Act of Parliament. A quarter of an hour elapsed, and there were no signs of moving. Minns looked at his watch for the sixth time.

"Coachman, are you going or not?" bawled Mr. Minns, with his head and half his body out of the coach window.

"Di—rectly, sir," said the coachman, with his hands in his pockets, looking as much unlike a man in a hurry as possible.

"Bill, take them cloths off." Five minutes more elapsed; at the end of which time the coachman mounted the box, from whence he looked down the street, and up the street, and hailed all the pedestrians for another five minutes.

"Coachman! if you don't go this moment, I shall get out," said Mr. Minns, rendered desperate by the lateness of the hour, and the impossibility of being in Poplar Walk at the appointed time.

"Going this minute, sir," was the reply; and, accordingly, the machine trundled on for a couple of hundred yards, and then stopped again. Minns doubled himself up in a corner of the coach, and abandoned himself to his fate, as a child, a mother, a bandbox, and a parasol became his fellow-passengers.

The child was an affectionate and an amiable infant: the little dear mistook Minns for his other parent, and screamed to embrace him.

"Be quiet, dear," said the mamma, restraining the

impetuosity of the darling, whose little fat legs were kicking and stamping, and twining themselves into the most complicated forms in an ecstasy of impatience. "Be quiet, dear, that's not your papa."

"Thank Heaven I am not!" thought Minns, as the first gleam of pleasure he had experienced that morning shone like a meteor through his wretchedness.

Playfulness was agreeably mingled with affection in the disposition of the boy. When satisfied that Mr. Minns was not his parent, he endeavoured to attract his notice by scraping his drab trousers with his dirty shoes, poking his chest with his mamma's parasol, and other nameless endearments peculiar to infancy, with which he beguiled the tediousness of the ride, apparently very much to his own satisfaction.

When the unfortunate gentleman arrived at the Swan, he found, to his great dismay, that it was a quarter-past five. The white house, the stables, the "Beware of the Dog"—every landmark was passed with a rapidity not unusual to a gentleman of a certain age when too late for dinner. After the lapse of a few minutes, Mr. Minns found himself opposite a yellow brick house with a green door, brass knocker and door-plate, green window frames and ditto railings, with "a garden" in front—that is to say, a small loose bit of gravelled ground, with one round and two scalene triangular beds, containing a fir-tree, twenty or thirty bulbs, and an unlimited number of marigolds. The taste of Mr. and Mrs. Budden was further displayed by the appearance

of a Cupid on each side of the door, perched upon a heap
of large chalk flints, variegated with pink conch-shells.
His knock at the door was answered by a stumpy boy
in drab livery, cotton stockings, and high-lows, who,
after hanging his hat on one of the dozen brass pegs
which ornamented the passage, denominated by cour-
tesy, "The Hall," ushered him into a front drawing-
room, commanding a very extensive view of the backs
of the neighbouring houses. The usual ceremony of
introduction, and so forth, over, Mr. Minns took his
seat—not a little agitated at finding that he was the
last comer, and, somehow or other, the Lion of about
a dozen people, sitting together in a small drawing-
room, getting rid of that most tedious of all time, the
time preceding dinner.

"Well, Brogson," said Budden, addressing an elderly
gentleman in a black coat, drab knee breeches, and long
gaiters, who, under pretence of inspecting the prints
in an Annual, had been engaged in satisfying himself
on the subject of Mr. Minns's general appearance, by
looking at him over the tops of the leaves—"well,
Brogson, what do Ministers mean to do? Will they go
out, or what?"

"Oh!—why—really, you know, I'm the last person
in the world to ask for news. Your cousin, from his
situation, is the most likely person to answer the question."

Mr. Minns assured the last speaker that, although he
was in Somerset House, he possessed no official com-

munication relative to the projects of His Majesty's Ministers. But his remark was evidently received incredulously; and no further conjectures being hazarded on the subject, a long pause ensued, during which the company occupied themselves in coughing and blowing their noses, until the entrance of Mrs. Budden caused a general rise.

The ceremony of introduction being over, dinner was announced, and down-stairs the party proceeded accordingly—Mr. Minns escorting Mrs. Budden as far as the drawing-room door, but being prevented, by the narrowness of the staircase, from extending his gallantry any farther. The dinner passed off as such dinners usually do. Ever and anon, amidst the clatter of knives and forks, and the hum of conversation, Mr. B.'s voice might be heard, asking a friend to take wine, and assuring him he was glad to see him; and a great deal of by-play took place between Mrs. B. and the servants, respecting the removal of the dishes, during which her countenance assumed all the variations of a weather-glass, from "stormy" to "set fair."

Upon the dessert and wine being placed on the table, the servant, in compliance with a significant look from Mrs. B., brought down "Master Alexander," habited in a sky-blue suit with silver buttons; and possessing hair of nearly the same colour as the metal. After sundry praises from his mother, and various admonitions as to his behaviour from his father, he was introduced to his godfather.

"Well, my little fellow—you are a fine boy, ain't you?" said Mr. Minns, as happy as a tomtit on birdlime.

"Yes."

"How old are you?"

"Eight, next We'nsday. How old are *you?*"

"Alexander," interrupted his mother, "how dare you ask Mr. Minns how old he is?"

"He asked me how old *I* was," said the precocious child, to whom Minns had from that moment internally resolved that he never would bequeath one shilling. As soon as the titter occasioned by the observation had subsided, a little smirking man with red whiskers, sitting at the bottom of the table, who during the whole of dinner had been endeavouring to obtain a listener to some stories about Sheridan, called out, with a very patronising air, "Alick, what part of speech is *be?*"

"A Verb."

"That's a good boy," said Mrs. Budden, with all a mother's pride. "Now, you know what a verb is?"

"A verb is a word which signifies to be, to do, or to suffer; as, I am—I rule—I am ruled. Give me an apple, ma."

"I'll give you an apple," replied the man with the red whiskers, who was an established friend of the family, or, in other words, was always invited by Mrs. Budden, whether Mr. Budden liked it or not, "if you'll tell me what is the meaning of *be*."

"Be?" said the prodigy, after a little hesitation. "An insect that gathers honey."

"No, dear," frowned Mrs. Budden; "B double E is the substantive."

"I don't think he knows much yet about *common* substantives," said the smirking gentleman, who thought this an admirable opportunity for letting off a joke. "It's clear he's not very well acquainted with *proper names*. He! he! he!"

"Gentlemen," called out Mr. Budden, from the end of the table, in a stentorian voice, and with a very important air, "will you have the goodness to charge your glasses? I have a toast to propose."

"Hear! hear!" cried the gentlemen, passing the decanters. After they had made the round of the table, Mr. Budden proceeded—"Gentlemen, there is an individual present——"

"Hear! hear!" said the little man with red whiskers.

"*Pray* be quiet, Jones," remonstrated Budden.

"I say, gentlemen, there is an individual present," resumed the host, "in whose society I am sure we must take great delight—and—and—the conversation of that individual must have afforded to every one present the utmost pleasure." ["Thank Heaven, he does not mean me!" thought Minns, conscious that his diffidence and exclusiveness had prevented his saying above a dozen words since he entered the house.] "Gentlemen, I am but a humble individual myself, and I perhaps ought to apologise for allowing any individual feelings of friendship and affection for the person I allude to, to induce me to venture to rise, to propose the health of that person—a person that I am sure—that is to say, a person whose virtues must endear him to those who know him—and those who have not the pleasure of knowing him cannot dislike him."

"Hear! hear!" said the company, in a tone of encouragement and approval.

"Gentlemen," continued Budden, "my cousin is a man who—who is a relation of my own." (Hear! hear!) Minns groaned audibly. "Who I am most happy to see here, and who, if he were not here, would certainly have deprived us of the great pleasure we all feel in seeing him. (Loud cries of hear!) Gentlemen, I feel that I have already trespassed on your attention for too long a time. With every feeling—of—with every sentiment of—of——"

"Gratification," suggested a friend of the family.

"—Of gratification, I beg to propose the health of Mr. Minns."

"Standing, gentlemen!" shouted the indefatigable little man with the whiskers—"and with the honours. Take your time from me, if you please. Hip! hip! hip!—Za!—Hip! hip! hip!—Za!—Hip! hip!—Za—a—a!"

All eyes were now fixed on the subject of the toast, who, by gulping down port wine at the imminent hazard of suffocation, endeavoured to conceal his confusion. After as long a pause as decency would admit, he rose, but, as the newspapers sometimes say in their reports, "we regret that we were quite unable to give even the substance of the honourable gentleman's observations." The words "present company—honour—present occasion," and "great happiness"—heard occasionally, and repeated at intervals, with a countenance expressive of the utmost confusion and misery, convinced the company that he was making an excellent speech; and, accordingly, on his resuming his seat, they cried "Bravo!" and manifested tumultuous applause. Jones, who had been long watching his opportunity, then darted up.

"Budden," said he, "will you allow *me* to propose a toast?"

"Certainly," replied Budden, adding, in an undertone to Minns right across the table, "Devilish sharp fellow that; you'll be very much pleased with his speech. He talks equally well on any subject." Minns bowed, and Mr. Jones proceeded:—

"It has on several occasions, in various instances, under many circumstances, and in different companies, fallen to my lot to propose a toast to those by whom, at the time, I have had the honour to be surrounded. I have sometimes, I will cheerfully own—for why should I deny it?—felt the overwhelming nature of the task I have undertaken, and my own utter incapability to do justice to the subject. If such have been my feelings, however, on former occasions, what must they be now—now—under the extraordinary circumstances in which I am placed! (Hear! hear!) To describe my feelings accurately would be impossible; but I cannot give you a better idea of them, gentlemen, than by referring to a circumstance which happens, oddly enough, to occur to my mind at the moment. On one occasion, when that truly great and illustrious man, Sheridan, was——"

Now, there is no knowing what new villainy in the form of a joke would have been heaped on the grave of that very ill-used man, Mr. Sheridan, if the boy in drab had not at that moment entered the room in a breathless state, to report that, as it was a very wet night, the nine-o'clock stage had come round, to know whether there was anybody going to town, as, in that case, he (the nine o'clock) had room for one inside.

Mr. Minns started up; and, despite countless exclamations of surprise and entreaties to stay, persisted in his determination to accept the vacant place. But the brown silk umbrella was nowhere to be found; and as the coachman couldn't wait, he drove back to the Swan, leaving word for Mr. Minns to "run round" and catch him. However, as it did not occur to Mr. Minns, for some ten minutes or so, that he had left the brown silk umbrella with the ivory handle in the other coach, coming down; and, moreover, as he was by no means remarkable for speed, it is no matter of surprise that, when he accomplished the feat of "running round" to the Swan, the coach—the last coach—had gone without him.

It was somewhere about three o'clock in the morning when Mr. Augustus Minns knocked feebly at the street-door of his lodgings in Tavistock Street, cold, wet, cross, and miserable. He made his will next morning, and his professional man informs us, in that strict confidence in which we inform the public, that neither the name of Mr. Octavius Budden, nor of Mrs. Amelia Budden, nor of Master Alexander Augustus Budden, appears therein.

MR. PICKWICK TAKES THE WORLD BY STORM
1836–1838

Chapter Two

MR. PICKWICK TAKES THE WORLD BY STORM

1836–1838

With the success of the *Sketches by Boz* running as a sort of serial in the London *Chronicle*, presently gathered into a volume, life opened out for young Charles Dickens with all the colours of the morning. To literary success was added a new personal happiness. One of his *Chronicle* editors, a Mr. George Hogarth, had a home adorned by three charming daughters. Dickens fell in love with the lot of them and became engaged to the eldest. A new stroke of literary fortune supplied the means of an early marriage. This was the appearance in the world of Mr. Pickwick, who may be said to have presided at the wedding of his creator with Catherine Hogarth (April 2, 1836).

It happened that there was in London a caricature artist called Robert Seymour, a man of gloom and depression combined, as it often is, with a rare sense of the comic. Seymour planned to draw a set of pictures to illustrate the misadventures of a group of Cockney sportsmen. The publishers, Chapman & Hall, liked the proposal, but added the idea of having sketches or stories written to go with the plates. Young "Boz" seemed to be the very man for it. They offered him fifteen guineas a month to write up the series in monthly parts. As Boz wrote to the Hogarth family, "The emolument was too tempting to resist." But he said to the publishers that he himself knew nothing of sport except "all kinds of locomotion"—supplied by his experience as a political reporter flying round in post chaises and such. So he suggested—the whole plan being very vague—a change of the sportsmen into a sort of "club," travelling round on a roving commission. Chapman & Hall said "Yes," and then, says Dickens, "I thought of Mr. Pickwick." This is as modest as if Dante had said, "Then I thought of Hell."

So the combination started to work. Seymour drew a long thin Pickwick; somebody else suggested a fat one, and there emerged at last the familiar figure of the genial, elderly Pickwick, dozing in a fishing punt.

Thus came into being the *Pickwick Papers*, the earlier chapters carrying the marks of their parentage in the baulking horses and the rook shooting and the exploits of Mr. Winkle. Poor Seymour's melancholy ended in suicide, with the enterprise just begun. Later on his relations claimed that he invented the *Pickwick Papers* and that they deserved a share of the resulting profits. Dickens was as touchy and indignant over this as he was at any form of criticism. From first to last he couldn't stand it. As a matter of fact Seymour's Cockney sportsmen had nothing to do with the success of Pickwick. The "papers" were at first a dismal failure. The sale of the opening numbers reached only about four hundred copies. The publishers very nearly scrapped the enterprise. It was only when Mr. Pickwick shook himself loose from Cockney sportsmen and entered upon a larger life of his own that the publication suddenly leaped into an abounding and phenomenal success. The sales before the end exceeded forty thousand for each number. The turning point seemed to come with the appearance of Mr. Samuel Weller, blacking the boots at the White Hart Inn, with whose existence there began a new world of English fiction.

This is the scene presented in the selection that follows. Mr. Pickwick and his club-mates, wandering at large, have picked up the companionship of that impecunious, shabby and persuasive rascal, Mr. Alfred Jingle, now enthroned as one of the world's immortals. Here was a character such as Dickens loved to draw, such as he alone could draw to perfection—crookedness turned by a soft haze of perspective into comicality, a rogue more precious than an honest man. Here begins that "divine retrospect" of Charles Dickens, the highest reach of his art; and with it came an instant recognition of the delighted public. Thus easily do we reach out to find our better selves. The Pickwickians, accompanied by Mr. Jingle, wander into the leafy hospitality of Dingley Dell—a very Utopia of good fellowship, presided over by the genius of rural England in the form of Mr. Wardle. Here all is wholesome and sustained enjoyment. Here among the Pickwickians and the younger ladies of Dingley Dell, Cupid strings his bow and feathers his arrows. But with the younger ladies is an elder—an autumn flower among the buds of spring—a maiden aunt. Cupid in those days was overyoung and overcritical. He shot his arrows at nothing over forty. Yet here, just on the border line, was the maiden aunt, and, to match her, a stout Pickwickian beau, Mr. Tracy Tupman. All might have gone well had not Mr. Jingle heard some whisper of a snug personal fortune attaching to the maiden aunt. She fell an easy victim to his persuasion. They elope, followed by the angry Wardle and the firm but indignant Pickwick in a flying chaise. The chase grows warm. It leads to London. It seeks the aid of Pickwick's lawyer, Mr. Perker, sharp as his very name. The pursuit ends at the White Hart Inn and with that the *Pickwick Papers* emerge into a larger life and a wider landscape with a vision of the law, the courts, the debtors and the grand romance beyond.

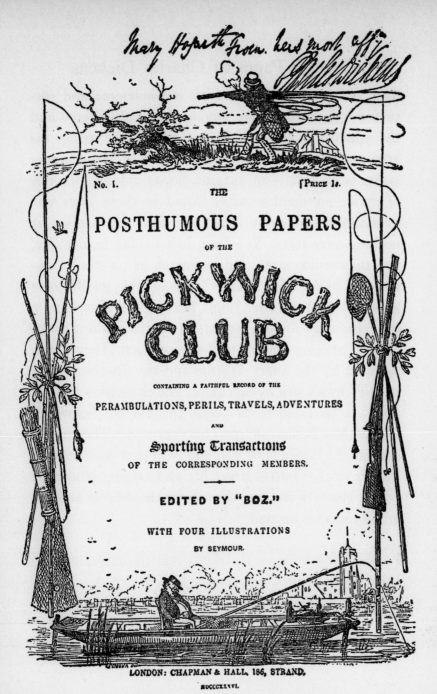

FACSIMILE OF PICKWICK COVER
(With Dickens's Autograph)

MR. SAMUEL WELLER AT THE WHITE HART INN

THERE ARE in London several old inns, once the head-quarters of celebrated coaches in the days when coaches performed their journeys in a graver and more solemn manner than they do in these times; but which have now degenerated into little more than the abiding and booking places of country wagons. The reader would look in vain for any of these ancient hostelries, among the Golden Crosses and Bull and Mouths, which rear their stately fronts in the improved streets of London. If he would light upon any of these old places, he must direct his steps to the obscurer quarters of the town, and there in some secluded nooks he will find several, still standing with a kind of gloomy sturdiness, amidst the modern innovations which surround them.

In the Borough especially, there still remain some half-dozen old inns, which have preserved their external features unchanged, and which have escaped alike the rage for public improvement and the encroachments of private speculation. Great, rambling, queer old places they are, with galleries, and passages, and staircases, wide enough and antiquated enough to furnish materials for a hundred ghost stories, supposing we should ever be reduced to the lamentable necessity of inventing any, and that the world should exist long enough to exhaust the innumerable veracious legends connected with old London Bridge, and its adjacent neighbourhood on the Surrey side.

It was in the yard of one of these inns—of no less celebrated a one than the White Hart—that a man was busily employed in brushing the dirt off a pair of boots, early on the morning succeeding the events narrated in the last chapter. He was habited in a coarse, striped waistcoat, with black calico sleeves, and blue glass buttons; drab breeches and leggings. A bright red handkerchief was wound in a very loose and unstudied style round his neck, and an old white hat was carelessly thrown on one side of his head. There were two rows of boots before him, one cleaned and the other dirty, and at every addition he made to the clean row, he paused from his work, and contemplated its results with evident satisfaction.

The yard presented none of that bustle and activity which are the usual characteristics of a large coach inn. Three or four lumbering wagons, each with a pile of goods beneath its ample canopy, about the height of the second-floor window of an ordinary house, were stowed away beneath a lofty roof which extended over one end of the yard; and another, which was probably to commence its journey that morning, was drawn out into the open space. A double tier of bedroom galleries, with old clumsy balustrades, ran round two sides of the straggling area, and a double row of bells to correspond, sheltered from the weather by a little sloping roof, hung over the door leading to the bar and coffee-room. Two or three gigs and chaise-carts were wheeled up under different little sheds and pent-houses; and the occasional heavy tread of a cart-horse, or rattling of a chain at the further end of the yard, announced to anybody who cared about the matter that the stable lay in that direction. When we add that a few boys in smock frocks were lying asleep on heavy packages, wool-packs, and other articles that were scattered about on heaps of straw, we have described as fully as need be the general appearance of the yard of the White Hart Inn, High Street, Borough, on the particular morning in question.

A loud ringing of one of the bells was followed by the appearance of a smart chambermaid in the upper sleeping gallery, who, after tapping at one of the doors, and receiving a request from within, called over the balustrades,—

"Sam!"

"Hallo," replied the man with the white hat.

"Number twenty-two wants his boots."

"Ask number twenty-two whether he'll have 'em now or wait till he gets 'em," was the reply.

"Come, don't be a fool, Sam," said the girl, coaxingly; "the gentleman wants his boots directly."

"Well, you *are* a nice young 'ooman for a musical party, you are," said the boot-cleaner. "Look at these here boots—eleven pair o' boots; and one shoe as b'longs to number six, with the wooden leg. The eleven boots is to be called at half-past eight and the shoe at nine. Who's number twenty-two, that's to put all the others out? No, no; regular rotation, as Jack Ketch said, wen he tied the men up. Sorry to keep you a-waitin', sir, but I'll attend to you directly."

Saying which, the man in the white hat set to work upon a top-boot with increased assiduity.

There was another loud ring; and the bustling old landlady of the White Hart made her appearance in the opposite gallery.

"Sam," cried the landlady, "where's that lazy, idle —why, Sam—oh, there you are; why don't you answer?"

"Vouldn't be gen-teel to answer, till you'd done talking," replied Sam gruffly.

"Here, clean them shoes for number seventeen directly, and take 'em to private sitting-room, number five, first floor."

The landlady flung a pair of lady's shoes into the yard, and bustled away.

"Number five," said Sam, as he picked up the shoes, and taking a piece of chalk from his pocket, made a memorandum of their destination on the soles—"Lady's shoes and private sittin'-room! I suppose *she* didn't come in the vagin."

"She came in early this morning," cried the girl, who was still leaning over the railing of the gallery, "with a gentleman in a hackney-coach, and it's him as wants his boots, and you'd better do 'em, that's all about it."

"Vy didn't you say so before," said Sam, with great indignation, singling out the boots in question from the heap before him. "For all I know'd he vas one o' the regular threepennies. Private room! and a lady too! If he's anything of a gen'lm'n, he's vurth a shillin' a day, let alone the arrands."

Stimulated by this inspiring reflection, Mr. Samuel brushed away with such hearty good-will, that in a few minutes the boots and shoes, with a polish which would have struck envy to the soul of the amiable Mr. Warren (for they used Day & Martin at the White Hart), had arrived at the door of number five.

"Come in," said a man's voice, in reply to Sam's rap at the door.

Sam made his best bow, and stepped into the presence of a lady and gentleman seated at breakfast. Having officiously deposited the gentleman's boots right and left at his feet, and the lady's shoes right and left at hers, he backed towards the door.

"Boots," said the gentleman.

"Sir," said Sam, closing the door, and keeping his hand on the knob of the lock.

"Do you know—what's a-name—Doctors' Commons?"

"Yes, sir."

"Where is it?"

"Paul's Churchyard, sir; low archway on the carriage side, bookseller's at one corner, hot-el on the other, and two porters in the middle as touts for licenses."

"Touts for licenses!" said the gentleman.

"Touts for licenses," replied Sam. "Two coves in vhite aprons—touches their hats ven you walk in—'License, sir, license?' Queer sort, them, and their mas'rs, too, sir—Old Bailey Proctors—and no mistake."

"What do they do?" inquired the gentleman.

"Do! *You*, sir! That ain't the worst on it, neither. They puts things into old gen'lm'n's heads as they never dreamed of. My father, sir, wos a coachman. A widower he wos, and fat enough for anything—uncommon fat, to be sure. His missus dies, and leaves him four hundred pound. Down he goes to the Commons, to see the lawyer and draw the blunt—very smart—top boots on—nosegay in his buttonhole—broadbrimmed tile—green shawl—quite the gen'lm'n. Goes through the archvay, thinking how he should inwest the money—up comes the touter, touches his hat—'License, sir, license?'—'What's that?' says my father.—'License, sir,' says he.—'What license?' says my father.—'Marriage license,' says the touter.—'Dash my veskit,' says my father, 'I never thought o' that.'—'I think you wants one, sir,' says the touter. My father pulls up, and thinks a bit—'No,' says he, 'damme, I'm too old, b'sides, I'm a many sizes too large,' says he.—'Not a bit on it, sir,' says the touter. —'Think not?' says my father.—'I'm sure not,' says he; 'we married a gen'lm'n twice your size, last Monday.'—'Did you, though?' said my father.—'To be sure, we did,' says the touter, 'you're a babby to him—this way, sir—this way!'—and sure enough my father walks arter him, like a tame monkey behind a horgan, into a little back office, vere a feller sat among dirty papers and tin boxes, making believe he was busy. 'Pray take a seat, vile I makes out the affidavit, sir?' says the lawyer.—'Thankee, sir,' says my father, and down he sat, and stared with all his eyes, and his mouth vide open, at the names on the boxes. 'What's your name, sir,' says the lawyer.—'Tony Weller,' says my father.—'Parish?' says the lawyer. 'Belle Savage,' says my father; for he stopped there wen he drove up, and he know'd nothing about parishes, *he* didn't.— 'And what's the lady's name?' said the lawyer. My father was struck all of a heap. 'Blessed if I know,' says he.—'Not know!' says the lawyer. 'No more nor you do,' says my father; 'can't I put that in arterwards?'— 'Impossible!' says the lawyer.—'Wery well,' says my father, after he'd thought a moment, 'put down Mrs. Clarke.'—'What Clarke?' says the lawyer, dipping his pen in the ink.—'Susan Clarke, Markis o' Granby, Dorking,' says my father; 'she'll have me, if I ask, I des-say—I never said nothing to her, but she'll have me, I know.'—The license was made out, and she *did* have him, and what's more she's got him now; and *I* never had any of the four hundred pound, worse luck. Beg your pardon, sir," said Sam, when he had concluded, "but wen I gets on this here grievance, I runs on like a new barrow vith the wheel greased." Having said which, and having paused for an instant to see whether he was wanted for anything more, Sam left the room.

"Half-past nine—just the time—off at once;" said the gentleman, whom we need hardly introduce as Mr. Jingle.

"Time—for what?" said the spinster aunt, coquettishly.

"Licence, dearest of angels—give notice at the church—call you mine to-morrow," said Mr. Jingle, and he squeezed the spinster aunt's hand.

"The license!" said Rachael, blushing.

"The license," repeated Mr. Jingle—

> "'*In hurry, post-haste for a license,*
> *In hurry, ding dong I come back.*'"

"How you run on!" said Rachael.

"Run on—nothing to the hours, days, weeks, months, years, when we're united—*run* on—they'll fly on—bolt—mizzle—steam-engine—thousand-horse power—nothing to it."

"Can't—can't we be married before to-morrow morning?" inquired Rachael.

"Impossible—can't be—notice at the church—leave the licence to-day—ceremony come off to-morrow."

"I am so terrified, lest my brother should discover us!" said Rachael.

"Discover—nonsense—too much shaken by the

breakdown—besides—extreme caution—gave up the post-chaise—walked on—took a hackney-coach—came to the Borough—last place in the world that he'd look in—ha! ha!—capital notion that—very."

"Don't be long," said the spinster, affectionately, as Mr. Jingle stuck the pinched-up hat on his head.

"Long away from *you?* Cruel charmer," and Mr. Jingle skipped playfully up to the spinster aunt, imprinted a chaste kiss upon her lips, and danced out of the room.

"Dear man!" said the spinster, as the door closed after him.

"Rum old girl," said Mr. Jingle, as he walked down the passage.

It is painful to reflect upon the perfidy of our species; and we will not, therefore, pursue the thread of Mr. Jingle's meditations as he wended his way to Doctors' Commons. It will be sufficient for our purpose to relate, that escaping the snares of the dragons in white aprons, who guard the entrance to that enchanted region, he reached the Vicar-General's office in safety, and having procured a highly flattering address on parchment, from the Archbishop of Canterbury, to his "trusty and well-beloved Alfred Jingle, and Rachael Wardle, greeting," he carefully deposited the mystic document in his pocket, and retraced his steps in triumph to the Borough.

He was yet on his way to the White Hart, when two plump gentlemen and one thin one entered the yard, and looked round in search of some authorized person of whom they could make a few inquiries. Mr. Samuel Weller happened to be at that moment engaged in burnishing a pair of painted tops, the personal property of a farmer who was refreshing himself with a slight lunch of two or three pounds of cold beef and a pot or two of porter, after the fatigues of the Borough market; and to him the thin gentleman straightway advanced.

"My friend," said the thin gentleman.

"You're one o' the adwice gratis order," thought Sam, "or you wouldn't be so wery fond o' me all at once." But he only said, "Well, sir."

"My friend," said the thin gentleman, with a conciliatory hem, "have you got many people stopping here now? Pretty busy. Eh?"

Sam stole a look at the inquirer. He was a little high-dried man, with a dark squeezed-up face, and small, restless, black eyes, that kept winking and twinkling on each side of his little inquisitive nose, as if they were playing a perpetual game of peep-bo with that feature. He was dressed all in black, with boots as shiny as his eyes, a low white neckcloth, and a clean shirt with a frill to it. A gold watch-chain, and seals, depended from his fob. He carried his black kid gloves *in* his hands, and not *on* them; and as he spoke, thrust his wrists beneath his coat tails, with the air of a man who was in the habit of propounding some regular posers.

"Pretty busy, eh?" said the little man.

"Oh, werry well, sir," replied Sam, "we shan't be bankrupts, and we shan't make our fort'ns. We eats our biled mutton without capers, and don't care for horse-radish ven ve can get beef."

"Ah," said the little man, "you're a wag, ain't you?"

"My eldest brother was troubled with that complaint," said Sam; "it may be catching—I used to sleep with him."

"This is a curious old house of yours," said the little man, looking round him.

"If you'd sent word you was a-coming, we'd ha' had it repaired;" replied the imperturbable Sam.

The little man seemed rather baffled by these several repulses, and a short consultation took place between him and the two plump gentlemen. At its conclusion, the little man took a pinch of snuff from an oblong silver box, and was apparently on the point of renewing the conversation, when one of the plump gentlemen, who in addition to a benevolent countenance, possessed a pair of spectacles, and a pair of black gaiters, interfered—

"The fact of the matter is," said the benevolent gentleman, "that my friend here (pointing to the other plump gentleman) will give you half a guinea, if you'll answer one or two——"

"Now, my dear sir—my dear sir," said the little man, "pray, allow me—my dear sir, the very first principle to be observed in these cases, is this: if you place the matter in the hands of a professional man, you must in no way interfere in the progress of the business; you must repose implicit confidence in him. Really, Mr." (he turned to the other plump gentleman, and said) —"I forget your friend's name."

"Pickwick," said Mr. Wardle, for it was no other than that jolly personage.

"Ah, Pickwick—really, Mr. Pickwick, my dear sir, excuse me—I shall be happy to receive any private suggestions of yours, as *amicus curiæ*, but you must see the impropriety of your interfering with my conduct in this case, with such an *ad captandum* argument as the offer of half a guinea. Really, my dear sir, really;" and the little man took an argumentative pinch of snuff, and looked very profound.

"My only wish, sir," said Mr. Pickwick, "was to bring this very unpleasant matter to as speedy a close as possible."

"Quite right—quite right," said the little man.

"With which view," continued Mr. Pickwick, "I made use of the argument which my experience of men has taught me is the most likely to succeed in any case."

"Ay, ay," said the little man, "very good, very good, indeed; but you should have suggested it to *me*. My dear sir, I'm quite certain you cannot be ignorant of the extent of confidence which must be placed in professional men. If any authority can be necessary on such a point, my dear sir, let me refer you to the well-known case in Barnwell and——"

FIRST APPEARANCE OF MR. SAMUEL WELLER

From an engraving by *Phiz*.

(HABLÔT KNIGHT BROWNE)

"Never mind George Barnwell," interrupted Sam, who had remained a wondering listener during this short colloquy; "everybody knows vhat sort of a case his was, tho' it's always been my opinion, mind you, that the young 'ooman deserved scragging a precious sight more than he did. Hows'ever, that's neither here nor there. You want me to accept of half a guinea. Wery well, I'm agreeable: I can't say no fairer than that, can I, sir?" (Mr. Pickwick smiled.) "Then the next question is, what the devil do you want with me, as the man said wen he see the ghost?"

"We want to know——" said Mr. Wardle.

"Now, my dear sir—my dear sir," interposed the busy little man.

Mr. Wardle shrugged his shoulders, and was silent.

"We want to know," said the little man, solemnly; "and we ask the question of you, in order that we may not awaken apprehensions inside—we want to know who you've got in this house at present?"

"Who there is in the house!" said Sam, in whose mind the inmates were always represented by that particular article of their costume, which came under his immediate superintendence. "There's a vooden leg in number six; there's a pair of Hessians in thirteen; there's two pair of halves in the commercial; there's these here painted tops in the snuggery inside the bar; and five more tops in the coffee-room."

"Nothing more?" said the little man.

"Stop a bit," replied Sam, suddenly recollecting himself. "Yes; there's a pair of Vellingtons a good deal worn, and a pair o' lady's shoes, in number five."

"What sort of shoes?" hastily inquired Wardle, who, together with Mr. Pickwick, had been lost in bewilderment at the singular catalogue of visitors.

"Country make," replied Sam.

"Any maker's name?"

"Brown."

"Where of?"

"Muggleton."

"It *is* them," exclaimed Wardle. "By heavens, we've found them."

"Hush!" said Sam. "The Vellingtons has gone to Doctors' Commons."

"No," said the little man.

"Yes, for a license."

"We're in time," exclaimed Wardle. "Show us the room; not a moment is to be lost."

"Pray, my dear sir—pray," said the little man; "caution, caution." He drew from his pocket a red silk purse, and looked very hard at Sam as he drew out a sovereign.

Sam grinned expressively.

"Show us into the room at once, without announcing us," said the little man, "and it's yours."

Sam threw the painted tops into a corner, and led the way through a dark passage, and up a wide staircase. He paused at the end of a second passage, and held out his hand.

"Here it is," whispered the attorney, as he deposited the money in the hand of their guide.

The man stepped forward a few paces, followed by the two friends and their legal adviser. He stopped at a door.

"Is this the room?" murmured the little gentleman.

Sam nodded assent.

Old Wardle opened the door; and the whole three walked into the room just as Mr. Jingle, who had that moment returned, had produced the license to the spinster aunt.

The spinster uttered a loud shriek, and, throwing herself in a chair, covered her face with her hands. Mr. Jingle crumpled up the license, and thrust it into his coat-pocket. The unwelcome visitors advanced into the middle of the room.

"You—you are a nice rascal, arn't you?" exclaimed Wardle, breathless with passion.

"My dear sir, my dear sir," said the little man, laying his hat on the table. "Pray, consider—pray. Defamation of character—action for damages. Calm yourself, my dear sir, pray——"

"How dare you drag my sister from my house?" said the old man.

"Ay—ay—very good," said the little gentleman, "you may ask that.—How dare you, sir?—eh, sir?"

"Who the devil are you?" inquired Mr. Jingle, in so fierce a tone that the little gentleman involuntarily fell back a step or two.

"Who is he, you scoundrel!" interposed Wardle. "He's my lawyer, Mr. Perker, of Gray's Inn.—Perker, I'll have this fellow prosecuted—indicted—I'll—I'll—I'll ruin him.—And you," continued Mr. Wardle, turning abruptly round to his sister, "you, Rachael, at a time of life when you ought to know better, what do *you* mean by running away with a vagabond, disgracing your family, and making yourself miserable? Get on your bonnet and come back.—Call a hackney-coach there, directly, and bring this lady's bill, d'ye hear—d'ye hear?"

"Cert'nly, sir," replied Sam, who had answered Wardle's violent ringing of the bell with a degree of celerity which must have appeared marvellous to anybody who didn't know that his eye had been applied to the outside of the keyhole during the whole interview.

"Get on your bonnet," repeated Wardle.

"Do nothing of the kind," said Jingle. "Leave the room, sir—no business here—lady's free to act as she pleases—more than one-and-twenty."

"More than one-and-twenty!" ejaculated Wardle contemptuously. "More than one-and-forty!"

"I ain't," said the spinster aunt, her indignation getting the better of her determination to faint.

"You are," replied Wardle; "you're fifty if you're an hour."

Here the spinster aunt uttered a loud shriek, and became senseless.

"A glass of water," said the humane Mr. Pickwick, summoning the landlady.

"A *glass* of water!" said the passionate Wardle. "Bring a bucket, and throw it all over her; it'll do her good, and she richly deserves it."

"Ugh, you brute!" ejaculated the kind-hearted landlady. "Poor dear." And with sundry ejaculations, of "Come now, there's a dear—drink a little of this—it'll do you good—don't give way so—there's a love," etc., etc., the landlady, assisted by a chambermaid, proceeded to vinegar the forehead, beat the hands, titillate the nose, and unlace the stays of the spinster aunt, and to administer such other restoratives as are usually applied by compassionate females to ladies who are endeavouring to ferment themselves into hysterics.

"Coach is ready, sir," said Sam, appearing at the door.

"Come along," cried Wardle. "I'll carry her downstairs."

At this proposition, the hysterics came on with redoubled violence.

The landlady was about to enter a very violent protest against this proceeding, and had already given vent to an indignant inquiry whether Mr. Wardle considered himself a lord of the creation, when Mr. Jingle interposed—

"Boots," said he, "get me an officer."

"Stay, stay," said little Mr. Perker. "Consider, sir, consider."

"I'll *not* consider," replied Jingle. "She's her own mistress—see who dares to take her away—unless she wishes it."

"I *won't* be taken away," murmured the spinster aunt. "I *don't* wish it." (Here there was a frightful relapse.)

"My dear sir," said the little man, in a low tone, taking Mr. Wardle and Mr. Pickwick apart—"my dear sir, we're in a very awkward situation. It's a distressing case—very—I never knew one more so; but really, my dear sir, really we have no power to control this lady's actions. I warned you before we came, my dear sir, that there was nothing to look to but a compromise."

There was a short pause.

"What kind of compromise would you recommend?" inquired Mr. Pickwick.

"Why, my dear sir, our friend's in an unpleasant position—very much so. We must be content to suffer some pecuniary loss."

"I'll suffer any rather than submit to this disgrace, and let her, fool as she is, be made miserable for life," said Wardle.

"I rather think it can be done," said the bustling little man.—"Mr. Jingle, will you step with us into the next room for a moment?"

Mr. Jingle assented, and the quartette walked into an empty apartment.

"Now, sir," said the little man, as he carefully closed

the door, "is there no way of accommodating this matter—step this way, sir, for a moment—into this window, sir, where we can be alone—there, sir, there, pray sit down, sir. Now, my dear sir, between you and I, we know very well, my dear sir, that you have run off with this lady for the sake of her money. Don't frown, sir, don't frown; I say, between you and I, *we* know it. We are both men of the world, and *we* know very well that our friends here are not—eh?"

Mr. Jingle's face gradually relaxed, and something distantly resembling a wink quivered for an instant in his left eye.

"Very good, very good," said the little man, observing the impression he had made. "Now the fact is, that beyond a few hundreds, the lady has little or nothing till the death of her mother—fine old lady, my dear sir."

"*Old*," said Mr. Jingle briefly but emphatically.

"Why, yes," said the attorney, with a slight cough. "You are right, my dear sir, she is *rather* old. She comes of an old family though, my dear sir; old in every sense of the word. The founder of that family came into Kent when Julius Cæsar invaded Britain—only one member of it, since, who hasn't lived to eighty-five, and *he* was beheaded by one of the Henrys. The old lady is not seventy-three now, my dear sir." The little man paused, and took a pinch of snuff.

"Well," cried Mr. Jingle.

"Well, my dear sir—you don't take snuff!—ah! so

much the better—expensive habit—well, my dear sir, you're a fine young man, man of the world—able to push your fortune, if you had capital, eh?"

"Well," said Mr. Jingle again.

"Do you comprehend me?"

"Not quite."

"Don't you think—now, my dear sir, I put it to you, *don't* you think—that fifty pounds and liberty would be better than Miss Wardle and expectation?"

"Won't do—not half enough!" said Mr. Jingle, rising.

"Nay, nay, my dear sir," remonstrated the little attorney, seizing him by the button. "Good round sum —a man like you could treble it in no time—great deal to be done with fifty pounds, my dear sir."

"More to be done with a hundred and fifty," replied Mr. Jingle coolly.

"Well, my dear sir, we won't waste time in splitting straws," resumed the little man, "say—say—seventy."

"Won't do," said Mr. Jingle.

"Don't go away, my dear sir—pray don't hurry," said the little man. "Eighty; come: I'll write you a cheque at once."

"Won't do," said Mr. Jingle.

"Well, my dear sir, well," said the little man, still detaining him; "just tell me what *will* do."

"Expensive affair," said Mr. Jingle. "Money out of pocket—posting, nine pounds; license, three—that's twelve—compensation, a hundred—hundred and twelve —breach of honour and—loss of the lady——"

"Yes, my dear sir, yes," said the little man, with a knowing look, "never mind the last two items. That's a hundred and twelve—say a hundred—come."

"And twenty," said Mr. Jingle.

"Come, come, I'll write you a cheque," said the little man; and down he sat at the table for that purpose.

"I'll make it payable the day after to-morrow," said the little man, with a look towards Mr. Wardle; "and we can get the lady away meanwhile." Mr. Wardle sullenly nodded assent.

"A hundred," said the little man.

"And twenty," said Mr. Jingle.

"My dear sir," remonstrated the little man.

"Give it him," interposed Mr. Wardle, "and let him go."

The cheque was written by the little gentleman, and pocketed by Mr. Jingle.

"Now, leave this house instantly!" said Wardle, starting up.

"My dear sir," urged the little man.

"And mind," said Mr. Wardle, "that nothing should have induced me to make this compromise—not even a regard for my family—if I had not known that the moment you got any money in that pocket of yours, you'd go to the devil faster, if possible, than you would without it——"

"My dear sir," urged the little man again.

"Be quiet, Perker," resumed Wardle.—"Leave the room, sir."

"Off directly," said the unabashed Jingle.—"By-by, Pickwick."

If any dispassionate spectator could have beheld the countenance of the illustrious man, whose name forms the leading feature of the title of this work, during the latter part of this conversation, he would have been almost induced to wonder that the indignant fire which flashed from his eyes did not melt the glasses of his spectacles, so majestic was his wrath. His nostrils dilated, and his fists clenched involuntarily, as he heard himself addressed by the villain. But he restrained himself again—he did *not* pulverize him.

"Here," continued the hardened traitor, tossing the license at Mr. Pickwick's feet; "get the name altered —take home the lady—do for Tuppy."

Mr. Pickwick was a philosopher, but philosophers are only men in armour, after all. The shaft had reached him, penetrated through his philosophical harness, to his very heart. In the frenzy of his rage, he hurled the inkstand madly forward, and followed it up himself. But Mr. Jingle had disappeared, and he found himself caught in the arms of Sam.

"Hollo," said that eccentric functionary, "furniter's cheap where you come from, sir. Self-acting ink, that 'ere; it's wrote your mark upon the wall, old gen'lm'n. Hold still, sir; wot's the use o' runnin' arter a man as has made his lucky, and got to t'other end of the Borough by this time?"

Mr. Pickwick's mind, like those of all truly great

men, was open to conviction. He was a quick and powerful reasoner; and a moment's reflection sufficed to remind him of the impotency of his rage. It subsided as quickly as it had been roused. He panted for breath, and looked benignantly round upon his friends.

Shall we tell the lamentations that ensued when Miss Wardle found herself deserted by the faithless Jingle? Shall we extract Mr. Pickwick's masterly description of that heartrending scene? His note-book, blotted with the tears of sympathising humanity, lies open before us; one word, and it is in the printer's hands. But, no! we will be resolute! We will not wring the public bosom, with the delineation of such suffering!

Slowly and sadly did the two friends and the deserted lady return next day in the Muggleton heavy coach. Dimly and darkly had the sombre shadows of a summer's night fallen upon all around, when they again reached Dingley Dell, and stood within the entrance to Manor Farm.

BOZ CONQUERS ENGLAND
1838–1841

Chapter Three

BOZ CONQUERS ENGLAND

1838–1841

THE PUBLICATION of the *Pickwick Papers* lifted Dickens from poverty to affluence and from isolation to world-wide popularity. In the history of English letters there had never been anything quite like the "Pickwick" boom. Men broke out into "Pickwick" coats and "Pickwick" hats. The "Pickwick" cigar became almost a national institution, involving the truly Pickwickian joke that the cigar was long and thin.

Charles Dickens made hay while the sun shone. He and Catherine were married (April 2, 1836) on the strength of the "tempting emolument." The grateful publishers later supplemented it with a sum of £2,500. The young couple set up house in highly genteel quarters in a colonnaded establishment called Furnival's Inn. Dickens's life was henceforth filled to the brim with congenial work, with the society of an increasing group of men of like mind, with long walks, endless (if one-sided) conversations, and dinners on this and that and every pretext at quaint old Greenwich inns and queer old city haunts. His domestic happiness was for a moment shattered by the sudden and tragic death of his sister-in-law, Mary Hogarth; but it was soon to be increased by the birth of his first-born son, Charles Dickens junior (January 6, 1837), and from now on he enjoyed in life all that goes with a full cradle and a babbling nursery. In all there were born ten children before the marriage broke in disaster and the fire upon the hearth burned to ashes.

Meantime, with Pickwick still running at full speed, Dickens undertook masses of other work, that strained even his exuberant vitality. He took on the job of editor of *Bentley's Miscellany*. He wrote in odd moments three or four little theatrical pieces, put on at St. James Theatre. He edited for Bentley a mass of biographical trash as the *Memoirs of Grimaldi the Clown*, and was surprised to see the public buy the stuff with eagerness. More than that, he began a new serial story called *Oliver Twist* (January, 1837) with Pickwick still running, and then another new one, *Nicholas Nickleby*, overlapping with Oliver. For all of this work his contracts were made with the reckless exuberance of youth. So it came about that the rapidly rising value of his books gave Dickens the idea that the publishers were a pack of crooks and himself a literary drudge hacking it at low wages. His peevish letters on this point are the first sign of that overstrain that eventually killed him.

Presently a still larger project opened up. Dickens planned to publish, not a single story, but as it were a

THE ORIGINAL "MASTER HUMPHREY'S CLOCK"
Formerly in the shop of William Humphrey, a clockmaker at Barnard Castle, Yorkshire. This time-piece suggested to Dickens the title for his twin stories known as *Master Humphrey's Clock*

whole cupboardful of stories at the same time. For this he invented the idea of Master Humphrey's clock— supposedly a piece of antique furniture in which old Master Humphrey has found a lot of manuscripts. These the old gentleman was supposed to read out to selected guests—Mr. Pickwick and Sam Weller being called back from immortality, most unconvincingly, to join their number. Thus did Dickens ever love what Samuel Weller called "wheels within wheels." But the scheme failed. When the public found that the *Clock* was not a single story, they found it too slow. Dickens saw the trouble, tricked Mr. Humphrey out of his clock and let his publication drift into the single narrative of *The Old Curiosity Shop*. When this was done the feeble-minded old Humphrey appeared again for an apologetic minute and wound up the clock with *Barnaby Rudge*. Then he expired, painlessly and unregretted.

But with *The Old Curiosity Shop* Dickens had already found again his full circle of eager listeners. More than that, he now added the conquest of America to that of England. *Pickwick* and *Oliver* and *Nicholas Nickleby* had met a roaring reception in the United States. But we are told that it was the fate and fortune of little Nell that gained for Dickens in America the place in the hearts of the people that he never lost. Bret Harte has chronicled this fact in the immortal verses in which he sorrowed for the death of Dickens.

Fewer people now read *The Old Curiosity Shop*. The

poignant theme, the unspeakable pathos of the child's death, lies aside from our present mood. Our literature lives upon sensation. But the age of Dickens lived on sentiment. It loved its own tears. It revelled in the luxury of sorrow. For indeed it needed them, to help to wash out the iniquities of the hard, cruel times that had preceded;—the days of the old vindictive law, the foul prisons, the convict hulks, the fettered slave, the brooding debtor eating out his heart in prison, and more than all, the cry of the children sobbing in the pauses of the clattering mill. On all these iniquities the Victorian tears fell soft as April rain, wearing down the ice of a Northern winter. No one can understand the age nor understand the work of Dickens who does not estimate the meaning of this environment. The depiction of such sorrow as the death of Little Nell and the death of little Paul Dombey we would not set down now, even if we had the hand and the art to do it. We would rather draw the blind and darken the room to hide the vision of the dying child; to shroud at least in darkened mystery the suffering for which we find no other consolation than despair.

Yet here let the picture—the death of Little Nell— stand as Dickens wrote it.

THE DEATH OF LITTLE NELL

(From THE OLD CURIOSITY SHOP)

THEY WERE all poor country people in the church, for the castle in which the old family had lived was an empty ruin, and there were none but humble folks for seven miles around. There, as elsewhere, they had an interest in Nell. They would gather round her in the porch, before and after service; young children would cluster at her skirts; and aged men and women forsake their gossips, to give her kindly greeting. None of them, young or old, thought of passing the child without a friendly word. Many who came from three or four miles distant brought her little presents; the humblest and rudest had good wishes to bestow.

She had sought out the young children whom she first saw playing in the churchyard. One of these— he who had spoken of his brother—was her little favourite and friend, and often sat by her side in the church, or climbed with her to the tower-top. It was his delight to help her, or to fancy that he did so, and they soon became close companions.

It happened that, as she was reading in the old spot by herself one day, this child came running in with his eyes full of tears, and after holding her from him, and looking at her eagerly for a moment, clasped his little arms passionately about her neck.

"What now?" said Nell, soothing him. "What is the matter?"

"She is not one yet!" cried the boy, embracing her still more closely. "No, no. Not yet."

She looked at him wonderingly, and putting his hair back from his face, and kissing him, asked what he meant.

"You must not be one, dear Nell," cried the boy. "We can't see them. They never come to play with us, or talk to us. Be what you are. You are better so."

"I do not understand you," said the child. "Tell me what you mean?"

"Why, they say," replied the boy, looking up into her face, "that you will be an angel before the birds sing again. But you won't be, will you? Don't leave us, Nell, though the sky *is* bright. Do not leave us!"

The child dropped her head, and put her hands before her face.

"She cannot bear the thought!" cried the boy, exulting through his tears. "You will not go. You know how sorry we should be. Dear Nell, tell me that you'll stay amongst us. Oh. Pray, pray, tell me that you will."

The little creature folded his hands, and kneeled down at her feet.

"Only look at me, Nell," said the boy, "and tell me that you'll stop, and then I shall know that they are wrong, and will cry no more. Won't you say yes, Nell?"

Still the drooping head and hidden face, and the child quite silent—save for the sobs.

"After a time," pursued the boy, trying to draw away her hand, "the kind angels will be glad to think that you are not among them, and that you stayed here to be with us. Willy went away to join them; but if he had known how I should miss him in our little bed at night, he never would have left me, I am sure."

Yet the child could make him no answer, and sobbed as though her heart were bursting.

"Why would you go, dear Nell? I know you would not be happy when you heard that we were crying for your loss. They say that Willy is in heaven now, and that it's always summer there, and yet I'm sure he grieves when I lie down upon his garden bed, and he cannot turn to kiss me. But if you do go, Nell," said the boy, caressing her, and pressing his face to hers, "be fond of him for my sake. Tell him how I love him still, and how much I loved you; and when I think that you two are together, and are happy, I'll try to bear it, and never give you pain by doing wrong—indeed I never will!"

The child suffered him to move her hands, and put them round his neck. There was a tearful silence, but it was not long before she looked upon him with a smile, and promised him, in a very gentle, quiet voice, that she would stay, and be his friend, as long as Heaven would let her.

* * * * *

Waving them off with his hand, and calling softly to her as he went, the old man stole into the room. They who were left behind drew close together, and, after a few whispered words—not unbroken by emotion, or easily uttered—followed him. They moved so gently that their footsteps made no noise; but there were sobs from among the group, and sounds of grief and mourning.

For she was dead. There, upon her little bed, she lay at rest. The solemn stillness was no marvel now.

She was dead. No sleep so beautiful and calm, so free from trace of pain, so fair to look upon. She seemed a creature fresh from the hand of God, and waiting for the breath of life; not one who had lived and suffered death.

Her couch was dressed with here and there some winter berries and green leaves, gathered in a spot she had been used to favour. "When I die, put near me something that has loved the light, and had the sky above it always." Those were her words.

She was dead. Dear, gentle, patient, noble Nell was dead. Her little bird—a poor, slight thing the pressure of a finger would have crushed—was stirring nimbly in its cage; and the strong heart of its child mistress was mute and motionless for ever.

Where were the traces of her early cares, her sufferings, and fatigues? All gone. Sorrow was dead indeed in her, but peace and perfect happiness were born— imaged in her tranquil beauty and profound repose.

THE DEATH OF LITTLE NELL

One of an extra set of plates by *Phiz*.

(HABLÔT KNIGHT BROWNE) 1848

And still her former self lay there, unaltered in this change. Yes. The old fireside had smiled upon that same sweet face; it had passed, like a dream, through haunts of misery and care; at the door of the poor schoolmaster on the summer evening, before the furnace fire upon the cold, wet night, at the still bedside of the dying boy, there had been the same mild, lovely look. So shall we know the angels in their majesty, after death.

The old man held one languid arm in his, and had the small hand tight folded to his breast, for warmth. It was the hand she had stretched out to him with her last smile—the hand that had led him on through all their wanderings. Ever and anon he pressed it to his lips; then hugged it to his breast again, murmuring that it was warmer now; and, as he said it, he looked, in agony, to those who stood around, as if imploring them to help her.

She was dead, and past all help, or need of it. The ancient rooms she had seemed to fill with life, even while her own was waning fast—the garden she had tended —the eyes she had gladdened—the noiseless haunts of many a thoughtful hour—the paths she had trodden, as it were, but yesterday—could know her never more.

"It is not," said the schoolmaster, as he bent down to kiss her on the cheek, and gave his tears free vent —"it is not on earth that Heaven's justice ends. Think what earth is, compared with the world to which her young spirit has winged its early flight; and say if one deliberate wish, expressed in solemn terms above this bed, could call her back to life, which of us would utter it!"

CHAPTER LXXII

When morning came, and they could speak more calmly on the subject of their grief, they heard how her life had closed.

She had been dead two days. They were all about her at the time, knowing that the end was drawing on. She died soon after daybreak. They had read and talked to her in the earlier portion of the night, but as the hours crept on she sank to sleep. They could tell, by what she faintly uttered in her dreams, that they were of her journeyings with the old man; they were of no painful scenes, but of people who had helped and used them kindly, for she often said, "God bless you!" with great fervour. Waking, she never wandered in her mind but once, and that was of beautiful music which she said was in the air. God knows. It may have been.

Opening her eyes at last, from a very quiet sleep, she begged that they would kiss her once again. That done, she turned to the old man with a lovely smile upon her face—such, they said, as they had never seen, and never could forget—and clung with both her arms around his neck. They did not know that she was dead, at first.

She had spoken very often of the two sisters, who, she said, were like dear friends to her. She wished they could be told how much she thought about them, and how she had watched them as they walked together by the riverside at night. She would like to see poor Kit, she had often said of late. She wished there was somebody to take her love to Kit. And, even then, she never thought or spoke about him, but with something of her old, clear, merry laugh.

For the rest, she had never murmured or complained; but, with a quiet mind, and manner quite unaltered— save that she every day became more earnest and more grateful to them—faded like the light upon a summer's evening.

The child who had been her little friend came there, almost as soon as it was day, with an offering of dried flowers, which he begged them to lay upon her breast. It was he who had come to the window overnight and spoken to the sexton, and they saw in the snow traces of small feet, where he had been lingering near the room in which she lay, before he went to bed. He had a fancy, it seemed, that they had left her there alone, and could not bear the thought.

He told them of his dream again, and that it was of her being restored to them, just as she used to be. He begged hard to see her, saying that he would be very quiet, and that they need not fear his being alarmed, for he had sat alone by his young brother all day long when *he* was dead, and had felt glad to be so near him. They let him have his wish; and, indeed, he kept his word, and was, in his childish way, a lesson to them all.

Up to that time, the old man had not spoken once
—except to her—or stirred from the bedside. But when
he saw her little favourite, he was moved as they had
not seen him yet, and made as though he would have
him come nearer. Then pointing to the bed, he burst
into tears for the first time, and they who stood by,
knowing that the sight of this child had done him good,
left them alone together.

Soothing him with his artless talk of her, the child
persuaded him to take some rest, to walk abroad, to do
almost as he desired him. And when the day came on,
which must remove her in her earthly shape from
earthly eyes for ever, he led him away, that he might
not know when she was taken from him.

They were to gather fresh leaves and berries for her
bed. It was Sunday—a bright, clear, wintry afternoon
—and as they traversed the village street, those who
were walking in their path drew back to make way
for them, and gave them a softened greeting. Some
shook the old man kindly by the hand, some stood un-
covered while he tottered by, and many cried, "God
help him!" as he passed along.

"Neighbour!" said the old man, stopping at the cottage where his young guide's mother dwelt, "how is it
that the folks are nearly all in black to-day? I have
seen a mourning ribbon or a piece of crape on almost
every one."

She could not tell, the woman said.

"Why, you yourself—you wear the colour too?"
he said. "Windows are closed that never used to be
by day. What does this mean?"

Again the woman said she could not tell.

"We must go back," said the old man hurriedly.
"We must see what this is."

"No, no," cried the child, detaining him. "Remember what you promised. Our way is to the old green
lane, where she and I so often were, and where you
found us more than once, making those garlands for
her garden. Do not turn back!"

"Where is she now?" said the old man. "Tell me
that."

"Do you not know?" returned the child. "Did we
not leave her but just now?"

"True. True. It *was* her we left—was it?"

He pressed his hand upon his brow, looked vacantly
round, and, as if impelled by a sudden thought, crossed
the road, and entered the sexton's house. He and his
deaf assistant were sitting before the fire. Both rose up,
on seeing who it was.

The child made a hasty sign to them with his hand.
It was the action of an instant, but that, and the old
man's look, were quite enough.

"Do you—do you bury any one to-day?" he said
eagerly.

"No, no! Who should we bury, sir?" returned the
sexton.

"Ay, who indeed? I say with you, who indeed?"

"It is a holiday with us, good sir," returned the sexton mildly. "We have no work to do to-day."

"Why, then, I'll go where you will," said the old man, turning to the child. "You're sure of what you tell me? You would not deceive me? I am changed, even in the little time since you last saw me."

"Go thy ways with him, sir," cried the sexton, "and Heaven be with ye both!"

"I am quite ready," said the old man meekly. "Come, boy, come;" and so submitted to be led away.

And now the bell—the bell she had so often heard, by night and day, and listened to with solemn pleasure almost as a living voice—rang its remorseless toll for her, so young, so beautiful, so good. Decrepit age, and vigorous life, and blooming youth, and helpless infancy, poured forth—on crutches, in the pride of strength and health, in the full blush of promise, in the mere dawn of life—to gather round her tomb. Old men were there, whose eyes were dim and senses failing—grandmothers, who might have died ten years ago, and still been old—the deaf, the blind, the lame, the palsied, the living dead in many shapes and forms, to see the closing of that early grave. What was the death it would shut in to that which still could crawl and creep above it!

Along the crowded path they bore her now; pure as the newly-fallen snow that covered it; whose day on earth had been as fleeting. Under the porch, where she had sat when Heaven in its mercy brought her to that peaceful spot, she passed again; and the old church received her in its quiet shade.

They carried her to an old nook, where she had many and many a time sat musing, and laid their burden softly on the pavement. The light streamed on it through the coloured window—a window where the boughs of trees were ever rustling in the summer, and where the birds sang sweetly all day long. With every breath of air that stirred among those branches in the sunshine, some trembling, changing light would fall upon her grave.

Earth to earth, ashes to ashes, dust to dust! Many a young hand dropped in its little wreath, many a stifled sob was heard. Some—and they were not a few—kneeled down. All were sincere and truthful in their sorrow.

* * * * *

They saw the vault covered, and the stone fixed down. Then, when the dusk of evening had come on, and not a sound disturbed the sacred stillness of the place—when the bright moon poured in her light on tomb and monument, on pillar, wall, and arch, and most of all (it seemed to them) upon her quiet grave— in that calm time, when outward things and inward thoughts teem with assurances of immortality, and worldly hopes and fears are humbled in the dust before them—then, with tranquil and submissive hearts they turned away, and left the child with God.

POEM BY BRET HARTE

ABOVE THE PINES *the moon was slowly drifting,*
  The river sang below;
The dim Sierras, far beyond, uplifting
  Their minarets of snow.

*   *   *   *   *

And then, while round them shadows gathered faster
  And as the firelight fell,
He read aloud the book wherein the Master
  Had wrote of Little Nell.

*   *   *   *   *

The fir-trees gathering closer to the shadows
  Listened in every spray,
While the whole camp with Nell on English meadows
  Wandered and lost their way.

*   *   *   *   *

AMERICA CONQUERS "BOZ"
1842

Chapter Four

AMERICA CONQUERS "BOZ"

1842

As if england was not enough for young "Boz" —for thus the world still loved to call him—he must set off to conquer America. Yet in England he seemed to have it all. He had moved into a fine house in Devonshire Terrace (1839). He had four completed books to his credit, and four children in the nursery. He had had (July, 1837) a ten days' romp on the Continent with his friends, and he shared in endless dinners and snug festivities.

But the thought of America fascinated him. Dickens, like most of the young men of his day who were not peers or squires or curates, was half a radical. He could find no place for dull old Tory gentlemen, impenetrable local magistrates, Eatonswill elections and the comic warfare of Coodle and Doodle against Foodle and Noodle, called the party system of England. There is in reality an intense bitterness behind the roaring fun of the Eatonswill elections in *Pickwick* and the comic pictures of the Bumbles and Squeerses and the dull-

witted justices of peace who represent the ingrained
tyranny of government overlong established and need-
ing only its quietus. Nor was even the monarchy in
those days safe and sacred to the rising generation.
The shabby exploits of George the Fourth had seen to
that.

Against this, Dickens set his picture of an imagined
America—a land of real freedom and equality, of simple
speech and equal birthright; a land which had said good-
bye to the mummeries of a court and the formalities of
an aristocracy and the tyranny of a privileged class.
"Thank God," Dickens had written in a fit of that
youthful despair and "world sorrow," which is probably a first touch of indigestion, "Thank God, there is
still Van Dieman's Land." There was perhaps another
reason for his going to America rather than to Tas-
mania. It is a legend, or a record, that Dickens had invested a part of his comfortable gains from his books
with a Western Land Company which had been selling
city lots in the Mississippi swamp called Cairo. These,
be it recalled, were the cheery days of the "roaring
forties" in America, with companies springing up like
mushrooms, banks breaking like pop-corn in a pan,
poverty and wealth, speculation and disaster, crookedness and optimism all jumbled up together in a fascinating mixture called national progress. They were
great days in which to live. It was still an empty world
with an unbounded horizon. The setting sun pointed
the way each evening to a golden west. There were

railways to make, acres in millions for the taking, every-thing still to do. What a world, as beside the poor shrunken area on which we live, all talking to itself on one radio, narrow and confined as a cattle pen—and the way out, to the next world, closed!

But Dickens when he came to America no more understood it than the moon. Here was in reality one of the great epics of human history, the vast invasion of the empty and fertile continent. But when Dickens went to what they called the "Far West," he saw nothing but dirt, discomfort, incivility and lack of manners, and had no vision of what was behind it. When he presently sent Martin Chuzzlewit to New Eden, decoyed by the prospectus of a land agent to a log hamlet in a Mississippi swamp, he did not realize that one day all the pictured town halls and exchanges and cathedrals would actually be brick. Martin Chuzzlewit left too soon. He could—quite literally—have stayed to take part in it all. In reality the smart Mr. Scudder had sold him a good thing.

Here stands from his own *American Notes* and from his *Martin Chuzzlewit* the progressive story of Dickens's disillusionment. It carried him from the exuberant gaiety of his arrival in Boston to his mournful denun-ciation of the Mississippi. Behind it all was his inborn horror of slavery, a thing he scarcely saw, a thing he would not see. Dickens was after all a Victorian, to whom even freedom to starve was better than life as a slave. He could not and would not ask whether the plantation slaves, working in the cornfield bathed in wind and sun, the little pickaninnies clinging to the red gowns of their mothers, were perhaps better off than the wan children in the gas light of the hideous factories of his own England.

AMERICAN NOTES FROM BOSTON TO NEW EDEN

(As in Chapter III of the AMERICAN NOTES *in part)*

WHEN I GOT into the streets upon this Sunday morning, the air was so clear, the houses were so bright and gay; the signboards were painted in such gaudy colours; the gilded letters were so very golden; the bricks were so very red, the stone was so very white, the blinds and area railings were so very green, the knobs and plates upon the street doors so marvellously bright and twinkling; and all so slight and unsubstantial in appearance—that every thoroughfare in the city looked exactly like a scene in a pantomime. It rarely happens in the business streets that a tradesman, if I may venture to call anybody a tradesman, where everybody is a merchant, resides above his store; so that many occupations are often carried on in one house, and the whole front is covered with boards and inscriptions. As I walked along, I kept glancing up at these boards, confidently expecting to see a few of them change into something; and I never turned a corner suddenly without looking out for the clown and pantaloon, who, I had no doubt, were hiding in a doorway or behind some pillar close at hand. As to Harlequin and Columbine, I discovered immediately that they lodged (they are always looking after lodgings in a pantomime) at a very small clockmaker's one storey high, near the hotel; which, in addition to various symbols and devices, almost covering the whole front, had a great dial hanging out—to be jumped through, of course.

The suburbs are, if possible, even more unsubstantial-looking than the city. The white wooden houses (so white that it makes one wink to look at them), with their green jalousie blinds, are so sprinkled and dropped about in all directions, without seeming to have any root at all in the ground; and the small churches and chapels are so prim, and bright, and highly varnished; that I almost believed the whole affair could be taken up piecemeal like a child's toy, and crammed into a little box.

The city is a beautiful one, and cannot fail, I should imagine, to impress all strangers very favourably. The private dwelling-houses are, for the most part, large and elegant; the shops extremely good; and the public buildings handsome. The State House is built upon the summit of a hill, which rises gradually at first, and afterwards by a steep ascent, almost from the water's edge. In front is a green inclosure, called the Common. The site is beautiful; and from the top there is a charming panoramic view of the whole town and neighbourhood. In addition to a variety of commodious offices, it contains two handsome chambers: in one the House of Representatives of the State hold their meetings; in the other, the Senate. Such proceedings as I saw here, were conducted with perfect gravity and decorum; and

were certainly calculated to inspire attention and respect.

There is no doubt that much of the intellectual re-
finement and superiority of Boston, is referable to the
quiet influence of the University of Cambridge, which
is within three or four miles of the city. The resident
professors at that university are gentlemen of learning
and varied attainments; and are, without one exception
that I can call to mind, men who would shed a grace
upon, and do honour to, any society in the civilized
world. Many of the resident gentry in Boston and its
neighbourhood, and I think I am not mistaken in adding, a large majority of those who are attached to the
liberal professions there, have been educated at this
same school. Whatever the defects of American uni-
versities may be, they disseminate no prejudices; rear
no bigots; dig up the buried ashes of no old supersti-
tions; never interpose between the people and their
improvement; exclude no man because of his religious
opinions; above all, in their whole course of study and
instruction, recognize a world, and a broad one too, lying beyond the college walls.

It was a source of inexpressible pleasure to me to observe the almost imperceptible, but not less certain
effect, wrought by this institution among the small
community of Boston; and to note at every turn the
humanising tastes and desires it has engendered; the affectionate friendships to which it has given rise; the
amount of vanity and prejudice it has dispelled. The

golden calf they worship at Boston is a pigmy compared with the giant effigies set up in other parts of that vast counting-house which lies beyond the Atlantic; and the almighty dollar sinks into something comparatively insignificant, amidst a whole Pantheon of better gods.

Above all, I sincerely believe that the public institutions and charities of this capital of Massachusetts are as nearly perfect, as the most considerate wisdom, benevolence, and humanity, can make them. I never in my life was more affected by the contemplation of happiness, under circumstances of privation and bereavement, than in my visits to these establishments.

*   *   *   *   *

(From Chapter XI American Notes, *in part)*

The *Messenger* was one among a crowd of high-pressure steamboats, clustered together by a wharf-side, which, looked down upon from the rising ground that forms the landing-place, and backed by the lofty bank on the opposite side of the river, appeared no larger than so many floating models. She had some forty passengers on board, exclusive of the poorer persons on the lower deck; and in half an hour, or less, proceeded on her way.

We had, for ourselves, a tiny stateroom with two berths in it, opening out of the ladies' cabin. There was, undoubtedly, something satisfactory in this "location," inasmuch as it was in the stern, and we had been a great many times very gravely recommended to keep as far aft as possible, "because the steamboats

generally blew up forward." Nor was this an unneces-
sary caution, as the occurrence and circumstances of
more than one such fatality during our stay sufficiently
testified. Apart from this source of self-congratulation,
it was an unspeakable relief to have any place, no matter how confined, where one could be alone; and, as the
row of little chambers of which this was one, had
each a second glass door besides that in the ladies'
cabin, which opened on a narrow gallery outside the
vessel, where the other passengers seldom came, and
where one could sit in peace and gaze upon the shifting
prospect, we took possession of our new quarters with
much pleasure.

If the native packets I have already described be unlike anything we are in the habit of seeing on water,
these western vessels are still more foreign to all the
ideas we are accustomed to entertain of boats. I hardly
know what to liken them to, or how to describe them.

In the first place, they have no mast, cordage, tackle,
rigging, or other such boat-like gear; nor have they
anything in their shape at all calculated to remind
one of a boat's head, stern, sides, or keel. Except that
they are in the water, and display a couple of paddle-
boxes, they might be intended, for anything that appears to the contrary, to perform some unknown service, high and dry, upon a mountain top. There is no
visible deck, even; nothing but a long, black, ugly roof,
covered with burned-out feathery sparks; above which
tower two iron chimneys, and a hoarse escape valve,

and a glass steerage-house. Then, in order as the eye descends towards the water, are the sides, and doors, and windows of the staterooms, jumbled as oddly together as though they formed a small street, built by the varying tastes of a dozen men; the whole is supported on beams and pillars resting on a dirty barge, but a few inches above the water's edge; and in the narrow space between this upper structure and this barge's deck, are the furnace fires and machinery, open at the sides to every wind that blows, and every storm of rain it drives along its path.

Passing one of these boats at night, and seeing the great body of fire, exposed as I have just described, that rages and roars beneath the frail pile of painted wood; the machinery, not warded off or guarded in any way, but doing its work in the midst of the crowd of idlers and emigrants and children, who throng the lower deck; under the management, too, of reckless men whose acquaintance with its mysteries may have been of six months' standing—one feels directly that the wonder is, not that there should be so many fatal accidents, but that any journey should be safely made.

Within, there is one long narrow cabin the whole length of the boat; from which the staterooms open, on both sides. A small portion of it at the stern is partitioned off for the ladies; and the bar is at the opposite extreme. There is a long table down the centre, and at either end a stove. The washing apparatus is forward, on the deck. It is a little better than on board the canal-boat, but not much. In all modes of travelling, the American customs, with reference to the means of personal cleanliness and wholesome ablution, are extremely negligent and filthy; and I strongly incline to the belief that a considerable amount of illness is referable to this cause.

We are to be on board the *Messenger* three days, arriving at Cincinnati (barring accidents) on Monday morning. There are three meals a day. Breakfast at seven, dinner at half-past twelve, supper about six. At each, there are a great many small dishes and plates upon the table, with very little in them; so that although there is every appearance of a mighty "spread," there is seldom really more than a joint; except for those who fancy slices of beet-root, shreds of dried beef, complicated entanglements of yellow pickle; maize, Indian corn, apple-sauce, and pumpkin.

Some people fancy all these little dainties together (and sweet preserves beside), by way of relish to their roast pig. They are generally those dyspeptic ladies and gentlemen who eat unheard-of quantities of hot corn bread (almost as good for the digestion as a kneaded pincushion), for breakfast, and for supper. Those who do not observe this custom, and who help themselves several times instead, usually suck their knives and forks meditatively, until they have decided what to take next; then pull them out of their mouths; put them in the dish; help themselves; and fall to work again. At dinner, there is nothing to drink upon the table,

Occasionally, we stop for a few minutes, maybe to take in wood, maybe for passengers, at some small town or village (I ought to say city, every place is a city here); but the banks are for the most part deep solitudes, overgrown with trees, which, hereabouts, are already in leaf and very green. For miles, and miles, and miles, these solitudes are unbroken by any sign of human life or trace of human footstep; nor is anything seen to move about them but the blue jay, whose colour is so bright, and yet so delicate, that it looks like a flying flower. At lengthened intervals, a log-cabin, with its little space of cleared land about it, nestles under a rising ground, and sends its thread of blue smoke curling up into the sky. It stands in the corner of the poor field of wheat, which is full of great unsightly stumps, like earthy butchers'-blocks. Sometimes the ground is only just now cleared; the felled trees lying yet upon the soil, and the log-house only this morning begun. As we pass this clearing, the settler leans upon his axe or hammer, and looks wistfully at the people from the world. The children creep out of the temporary hut, which is like a gipsy tent upon the ground, and clap their hands and shout. The dog only glances round at us, and then looks up into his master's face again, as if he were rendered uneasy by any suspension of the common business, and had nothing more to do with pleasurers. And still there is the same eternal foreground. The river has washed away its banks, and stately trees have fallen down into the stream. Some have been there so long, that they are mere dry grizzly skeletons. Some have just toppled over, and having earth yet above their roots, are bathing their green heads in the river, and putting forth new shoots and branches. Some are almost sliding down, as you look at them. And some were drowned so long ago, that their bleached arms start out from the middle of the current, and seem to try to grasp the boat, and drag it under water.

Through such a scene as this, the unwieldy machine takes its hoarse, sullen way, venting, at every revolution of the paddles, a loud high-pressure blast; enough, one would think, to waken up the host of Indians who lie buried in a great mound yonder, so old, that mighty oaks and other forest trees have struck their roots into its earth; and so high, that it is a hill, even among the hills that Nature planted round it. The very river, as though it shared one's feelings of compassion for the extinct tribes who lived so pleasantly here, in their blessed ignorance of white existence, hundreds of years ago, steals out of its way to ripple near this mound; and there are few places where the Ohio sparkles more brightly than in the Big Grave Creek.

(*From a letter to* MACREADY, *March 22, 1842*)

... FREEDOM of opinion! Macready, if I had been born here and had written my books in this country, producing them with no stamp of approval from any other land, it is my solemn belief that I should have lived and died poor, unnoticed and a "black sheep" to boot. I never was more convinced of anything than I am of that.

The people are affectionate, generous, open-hearted, hospitable, enthusiastic, good-humoured, anxious to oblige, far less prejudiced than they have been described to be, frequently polished and refined, very seldom rude or disagreeable. I have made a great many friends here, even in public conveyances, whom I have been truly sorry to part from. In the towns I have formed perfect attachments. I have seen none of that greediness and indecorousness on which travellers have laid so much emphasis. I have returned frankness with frankness; met questions not intended to be rude, with answers meant to be satisfactory; and have not spoken to one man, woman, or child of any degree who has not grown positively affectionate before we parted. In the respect of not being left alone, and of being horribly disgusted by tobacco chewing and tobacco spittle, I have suffered considerably. The sight of slavery in Virginia, the hatred of British feeling upon the subject, and the miserable hints of the impotent indignation of the South, have pained me much; on the last head, of course, I have felt nothing but a mingled pity and amusement; on the other sheer distress. But however much I like the ingredients of this great dish, I cannot but come back to the point upon which I started, and say that the dish itself goes against the grain with me, and that I don't like it.

(From a letter to MR. HENRY AUSTIN, *May 1, 1842)*

Is IT NOT a horrible thing that scoundrel booksellers should grow rich here from publishing books, the authors of which do not reap one farthing from their issue by scores of thousands; and that every vile, blackguard, and detestable newspaper, so filthy and bestial that no honest man would admit one into his house for a scullery door-mat, should be able to publish those same writings side by side, cheek by jowl, with the coarsest and most obscene companions with which they must become connected, in course of time, in people's minds? Is it tolerable that besides being robbed and rifted an author should be forced to appear in any form, in any vulgar dress, in any atrocious company; that he should have no choice of his audience, no control over his own distorted text, and that he should be compelled to jostle out of the course the best men in this country who only ask to live by writing? I vow before high heaven that my blood so boils at these enormities, that when I speak about them I seem to grow twenty feet high, and to swell out in proportion. "Robbers that ye are," I think to myself when I get upon my legs, "here goes!"

(From a letter to THOMAS MITTON, *January 31, 1842)*

I CAN GIVE you no conception of my welcome here. There never was a king or emperor upon the earth so cheered and followed by crowds, and entertained in public at splendid balls and dinners, and waited on by public bodies and deputations of all kinds. I have had one from the Far West—a journey of two thousand miles! If I go out in a carriage, the crowds surround it and escort me home; if I go to the theatre, the whole house (crowded to the roof) rises as one man, and the timbers ring again. You cannot imagine what it is. I have five great public dinners on hand at this moment, and invitations from every town and village and city in the States.

(*From* MARTIN CHUZZLEWIT, *Chapter XXIII*)

AFTER THAT he turned away, and walked to and fro upon the deck full two hours. Nor did he speak again, except to say "Good-night," until next day; nor even then upon this subject, but on other topics quite foreign to the purpose.

As they proceeded further on their track, and came more and more towards their journey's end, the monotonous desolation of the scene increased to that degree, that for any redeeming feature it presented to their eyes, they might have entered, in the body, on the grim domains of Giant Despair. A flat morass, bestrewn with fallen timber; a marsh on which the good growth of the earth seemed to have been wrecked and cast away, that from its decomposing ashes vile and ugly things might rise; where the very trees took the aspect of huge weeds, begotten of the slime from which they sprung, by the hot sun that burnt them; where fatal maladies, seeking whom they might infect, came forth at night, in misty shapes, and creeping out upon the water, hunted them like spectres until day; where even the blessed sun, shining down on festering elements of corruption and disease, became a horror; this was the realm of Hope through which they moved.

At last they stopped. At Eden too. The waters of the Deluge might have left it but a week before, so choked with slime and matted growth was the hideous swamp which bore that name.

There being no depth of water close in shore, they landed from the vessel's boat, with all their goods beside them. There were a few log-houses visible among the dark trees—the best, a cow-shed or a rude stable. But for the wharves, the market-place, the public buildings!

"Here comes an Edener," said Mark. "He'll get us help to carry these things up. Keep a good heart, sir. Hallo there!"

The man advanced toward them through the thickening gloom, very slowly, leaning on a stick. As he drew nearer, they observed that he was pale and worn, and that his anxious eyes were deeply sunken in his head. His dress of homespun blue hung about him in rags. His feet and head were bare. He sat down on a stump half-way, and beckoned them to come to him. When they complied, he put his hand upon his side as if in pain, and while he fetched his breath stared at them, wondering.

"Strangers!" he exclaimed, as soon as he could speak.

"The very same," said Mark. "How are you, sir?"

"I've had the fever very bad," he answered faintly. "I haven't stood upright these many weeks. Those are your notions, I see," pointing to their property.

"Yes, sir," said Mark, "they are. You couldn't recommend us someone as would lend a hand to help carry 'em up to the—to the town, could you, sir?"

"My eldest son would do it if he could," replied the man; "but to-day he has his chill upon him, and is lying wrapped up in the blankets. My youngest died last week."

"I'm sorry for it, governor, with all my heart," said Mark, shaking him by the hand. "Don't mind us. Come along with me, and I'll give you an arm back. The goods is safe enough, sir,"—to Martin—"there ain't many people about, to make away with 'em. What a comfort that is!"

"No," cried the man. "You must look for such folk here," knocking his stick upon the ground, "or yonder in the bush, towards the north. We've buried most of 'em. The rest have gone away. Them that we have here don't come out at night."

"The night air ain't quite wholesome, I suppose?" said Mark.

"It's deadly poison," was the settler's answer.

Mark showed no more uneasiness than if it had been commended to him as ambrosia; but he gave the man his arm, and as they went along explained to him the nature of their purchase, and inquired where it lay. Close to his own log-house, he said; so close that he had used their dwelling as a store-house for some corn; they must excuse it that night, but he would endeavour to get it taken out upon the morrow. He then gave them to understand, as an additional scrap of local chit-chat, that he had buried the last proprietor with his own hands; a piece of information which Mark also received without the least abatement of his equanimity.

In a word, he conducted them to a miserable cabin, rudely constructed of the trunks of trees; the door of which had either fallen down or been carried away long ago; and which was consequently open to the wild landscape and the dark night. Saving for the little store he had mentioned, it was perfectly bare of all furniture; but they had left a chest upon the landing-place, and he gave them a rude torch in lieu of candle. This latter acquisition Mark planted in the earth, and then declaring that the mansion "looked quite comfortable," hurried Martin off again to help bring up the chest. And all the way to the landing-place and back, Mark talked incessantly, as if he would infuse into his partner's breast some faint belief that they had arrived under the most auspicious and cheerful of all imaginable circumstances.

But many a man who would have stood within a home dismantled, strong in his passion and design of vengeance, has had the firmness of his nature conquered by the razing of an air-built castle. When the log-hut received them for the second time, Martin lay down upon the ground, and wept aloud.

"Lord love you, sir!" cried Mr. Tapely, in great terror; "don't do that! Don't do that, sir! Anything but that! It never helped man, woman, or child over the lowest fence yet, sir, and never will. Besides it being of no use to you, it's worse than of no use to me, for the least sound of it will knock me flat down. I can't stand up agin it, sir. Anything but that!"

There is no doubt he spoke the truth, for the extraordinary alarm with which he looked at Martin as he paused upon his knees before the chest, in the act of unlocking it, to say these words, sufficiently confirmed him.

"I ask your forgiveness a thousand times, my dear fellow," said Martin. "I couldn't have helped it, if death had been the penalty."

"Ask my forgiveness!" said Mark with his accustomed cheerfulness, as he proceeded to unpack the chest. "The head partner a-asking forgiveness of Co., eh? There must be something wrong in the firm when that happens. I must have the books inspected, and the accounts gone over immediate. Here we are. Everything in its proper place. Here's the salt pork. Here's the biscuit. Here's the whisky—uncommon good it smells too. Here's the tin pot. This tin pot's a small fortun' in itself! Here's the blankets. Here's the axe. Who says we ain't got a first-rate fit-out? I feel as if I was a cadet gone out to Indy, and my noble father was chairman of the Board of Directors. Now, when I've got some water from the stream afore the door and

mixed the grog," cried Mark, running out to suit the
action to the word, "there's a supper ready, comprising
every delicacy of the season. Here we are, sir, all com-
plete. For what we are going to receive, et cetrer. Lord
bless you, sir, it's very like a gipsy party!"

It was impossible not to take heart, in the company
of such a man as this. Martin sat upon the ground beside the box, took out his knife, and ate and drank
sturdily.

"Now you see," said Mark, when they had made a
hearty meal; "with your knife and mine, I sticks this
blanket right afore the door, or where, in a state of high
civilisation, the door would be. And very neat it looks.
Then I stops the aperture below, by putting the chest
agin it. And very neat *that* looks. Then there's your
blanket, sir. Then here's mine. And what's to hinder our
passing a good night?"

For all his light-hearted speaking, it was long before
he slept himself. He wrapped his blanket round him,
put the axe ready to his hand, and lay across the
threshold of the door; too anxious and too watchful to
close his eyes. The novelty of their dreary situation, the
dread of some rapacious animal or human enemy, the
terrible uncertainty of their means of subsistence, the
apprehension of death, the immense distance and the
hosts of obstacles between themselves and England,
were fruitful sources of disquiet in the deep silence of
the night. Though Martin would have had him think
otherwise, Mark felt that he was waking also, and a

prey to the same reflections. This was almost worse than all, for if he began to brood over their miseries instead of trying to make head against them, there could be little doubt that such a state of mind would powerfully assist the influence of the pestilent climate. Never had the light of day been half so welcome to his eyes, as when, awaking from a fitful doze, Mark saw it shining through the blanket in the doorway.

He stole out gently, for his companion was sleeping now; and having refreshed himself by washing in the river, where it flowed before the door, took a rough survey of the settlement. There were not above a score of cabins in the whole; half of these appeared un-tenanted; all were rotten and decayed. The most totter-ing, abject, and forlorn among them, was called with great propriety, the Bank and National Credit Office. It had some feeble props about it, but was settling deep down in the mud, past all recovery.

Here and there, an effort had been made to clear the land, and something like a field had been marked out, where, among the stumps and ashes of burnt trees, a scanty crop of Indian corn was growing. In some quarters, a snake or zigzag fence had been begun, but in no instance had it been completed; and the fallen logs, half hidden in the soil, lay mouldering away. Three or four meagre dogs, wasted and vexed with hunger; some long-legged pigs, wandering away into the woods in search of food; some children, nearly naked, gazing at him from the huts; were all the living things he saw.

A fœtid vapour, hot and sickening as the breath of an oven, rose up from the earth, and hung on everything around; and as his footprints sank into the marshy ground, a black ooze started forth to blot them out.

Their own land was mere forest. The trees had grown so thick and close that they shouldered one another out of their places, and the weakest, forced into shapes of strange distortion, languished like cripples. The best were stunted, from the pressure and the want of room; and high about the stems of all, grew long rank grass, dank weeds, and frowsy underwood; not divisible into their separate kinds, but tangled all together in a heap; a jungle deep and dark, with neither earth nor water at its roots, but putrid matter, formed of the pulpy offal of the two, and of their own corruption.

He went down to the landing-place where they had left their goods last night; and there he found some half-dozen men—wan and forlorn to look at, but ready enough to assist—who helped him to carry them to the log-house. They shook their heads in speaking of the settlement, and had no comfort to give him. Those who had the means of going away, had all deserted it. They who were left had lost their wives, their children, friends, or brothers there, and suffered much themselves. Most of them were ill then; none were the men they had been once. They frankly offered their assistance and advice, and, leaving him for that time, went sadly off upon their several tasks.

Martin was by this time stirring; but he had greatly

changed, even in one night. He was very pale and languid; he spoke of pains and weakness in his limbs, and complained that his sight was dim, and his voice feeble. Increasing in his own briskness as the prospect grew more and more dismal, Mark brought away a door from one of the deserted houses, and fitted it to their own habitation; they went back again for a rude bench he had observed, with which he presently returned in triumph; and having put this piece of furniture outside the house, arranged the notable tin-pot and other such movables upon it, that it might represent a dresser or a sideboard. Greatly satisfied with this arrangement, he next rolled their cask of flour into the house, and set it up on end in one corner, where it served for a side-table. No better dining-table could be required than the chest, which he solemnly devoted to that useful service thenceforth. Their blankets, clothes, and the like, he hung on pegs and nails. And lastly, he brought forth a great placard (which Martin in the exultation of his heart had prepared with his own hands at the National Hotel), bearing the inscription, CHUZZLEWIT & CO., ARCHITECTS AND SURVEYORS, which he displayed upon the most conspicuous part of the premises, with as much gravity as if the thriving city of Eden had a real existence, and they expected to be overwhelmed with business.

"These here tools," said Mark, bringing forward Martin's case of instruments, and sticking the compasses upright in a stump before the door, "shall be

THE THRIVING CITY OF EDEN AS IT APPEARED IN FACT

From an engraving by *Phiz*.

set out in the open air to show that we come provided. And now if any gentleman wants a house built, he'd better give his orders, before we're otherways bespoke."

Considering the intense heat of the weather, this was not a bad morning's work; but without pausing for a moment, though he was streaming at every pore, Mark vanished into the house again, and presently reappeared with a hatchet; intent on performing some impossibilities with that implement.

"Here's a ugly old tree in the way, sir," he observed, "which'll be all the better down. We can build the oven in the afternoon. There never was such a handy spot for clay as Eden is. That's convenient anyhow."

But Martin gave him no answer. He had sat the whole time with his head upon his hands, gazing at the current as it rolled swiftly by; thinking, perhaps, how fast it moved towards the open sea, the highroad to the home he never would behold again.

Not even the vigorous strokes which Mark dealt at the tree awoke him from his mournful meditation. Finding all his endeavours to rouse him of no use, Mark stopped in his work and came towards him.

"Don't give in, sir," said Mr. Tapley.

"Oh, Mark," returned his friend, "what have I done in all my life that has deserved this heavy fate?"

"Why, sir," returned Mark, "for the matter of that, ev'rybody as is here might say the same thing; many of 'em with better reason, p'raps, than you or me. Hold up, sir. Do something. Couldn't you ease your mind, now, don't you think, by making some personal obserwations in a letter to Scadder?"

"No," said Martin, shaking his head sorrowfully—"I am past that."

"But if you're past that already," returned Mark, "you must be ill, and ought to be attended to."

"Don't mind me," said Martin. "Do the best you can for yourself. You'll soon have only yourself to consider. And then God speed you home, and forgive me for bringing you here! I am destined to die in this place. I felt it the instant I set foot upon the shore. Sleeping or waking, Mark, I dreamed it all last night."

"I said you must be ill," returned Mark tenderly, "and now I'm sure of it. A touch of fever and ague caught on these rivers, I daresay; but bless you, *that's* nothing. It's only a seasoning; and we must all be seasoned, one way or another. That's religion, that is, you know," said Mark.

He only sighed and shook his head.

"Wait half a minute," said Mark cheerily, "till I run up to one of our neighbours and ask what's best to be took, and borrow a little of it to give you; and to-morrow you'll find yourself as strong as ever again. I won't be gone a minute. Don't give in while I'm away, whatever you do!"

Throwing down his hatchet, he sped away immediately, but stopped when he had got a little distance, and looked back—then hurried on again.

"Now, Mr. Tapley," said Mark, giving himself a

tremendous blow in the chest, by way of reviver, "just you attend to what I've got to say. Things is looking about as bad as they *can* look, young man. You'll not have such another opportunity for showing your jolly disposition, my fine fellow, as long as you live. And therefore, Tapley, Now's your time to come out strong; or Never!"

DICKENS INVADES EUROPE
1842–1846

Chapter Five

DICKENS INVADES EUROPE
1842–1846

DICKENS returned from America in a burst of enthusiasm for home and England. He signalized it by a holiday trip to Cornwall with his bosom friends, John Foster—later his biographer—and the artists Stanfield and Maclise. It was a sort of schoolboy holiday, exuberant with merriment. After that Dickens settled down to write his *American Notes* (1842), setting forth, as seen, his cheery views on the new republic. The next year saw him busy on *Martin Chuzzlewit*, the story flowing from an easy pen. When public interest in the tale seemed to slacken, Dickens shipped Martin off to America. This was done quite without previous plan or premeditation. For Dickens there were no rules of art—other than the rules that govern song-birds. He had no idea at the start what was going to happen to Mr. Pickwick and quite resented the later accusation that Mr. Pickwick visibly alters from something like an amiable idiot to a sagacious British gentleman. In the same way he stopped the actions of

Barnaby Rudge for five years and kept all the characters marking time—a cruel trick to play on the heroine. But Dickens had thought of putting in the Lord George Gordon Riots of 1780, and the story had started five years too soon for them. After this it was a mere nothing to run Martin Chuzzlewit out to America and send him West, as already seen, to settle on Dickens's own swamp lots in Cairo.

But at the close of that year (1843) Dickens opened up a new line of writing, on which henceforth rested a large part of his work, and a large part of the affection which his work inspired. This was his famous *Christmas Carol*, the first of the long series of his Christmas books, and of the special Christmas numbers of his later magazines. Dickens did not invent "Christmas stories" and "Christmas numbers," but he went a long way towards giving them the place in English and American life that they have ever since enjoyed. He had already touched the rich vein of Christmas sentiment with the winter scenes at Dingley Dell. The *Carol* he wrote in a sort of rhapsody, as Rouget de l'Isle composed the "Marseillaise," and Coleridge dreamed his "Kubla Khan."

All the world knows the story at first, or second or third hand—in adaptations, in dramas and in pictures. Few still read it with the original and proper accompaniment of ghost and groans. The Victorian spectres have worn thin and pathetic beside the rapidity of "Mickey Mouse" and the transformations of the moving picture. But the base of it still remains, the transformation of the bad to the good, old as the miracles and opening the windows of the Kingdom of Heaven. Such is the vision of the redeemed Scrooge calling from his window on a frosty Christmas morning.

Here was Scrooge, "a squeezing, wrenching, grasping, scraping, clutching, covetous old sinner!" But the spectres have visited him and the ghosts have shown him what is what. The scales have fallen from his clouded eyes, and he looks out upon the new sunlight of a Christmas morning—still in time, still in time! That is the true Dickens feeling, that Scrooge is still just in time! and the past can still be redeemed! All through Dickens runs this theme of redemption just in time, atonement still in time for its award. Dickens knew by instinct that the "happy ending," the one thing that life denies us, is the very soul of fiction. Thus stood Scrooge at his window, gazing out upon an altered world and one that any of us may enter by throwing open the windows of the soul.

The *Christmas Carol* was, and remains, a vast literary success. But financially it failed to come up to the rosy expectations which Dickens had now learned to cultivate. He had "set his heart" on a thousand pounds and only got about seven hundred. He was getting rich enough to worry over money. So, in a sudden panic of economy, he must needs take his wife and her sister with four children off to Europe for a cheap year on the Continent. A hugh barouche was specially built (£45) and transported across the Channel. In it the family (July, 1844), with a courier and postilions, went rolling through the sunny vineyards of France. France, which from now on became almost Dickens's home, seems to have had a fascination for him. He never was able to take it quite seriously: the picturesque costumes, the sunlit scene, the odd language, the polite people, all carried for him a sort of make-believe. Even when he exchanged the lighter pictures of his remembered tours for the sombre tragedy of his imagined *Tale of Two Cities*, there was still an element of stage effect, as of thunder behind the scene. Italy, of which he had known nothing, awoke him to sudden admirations, the more so as the glories of Venice and the majesty of Rome came to him as a sort of personal discovery. But whether in Switzerland, Genoa or Paris, Dickens still lived the sights and sounds of London. That—and with it the English countryside—was his inspiration. The Continent was just colour. Thus did his fancy picture from his Swiss sojourn the Christmas streets of London and his ear catch the calling of the Christmas *Chimes* that made his second Christmas story. So filled up with it was he that he must needs post from Switzerland to London (December 2, 1844) for the fun of reading it to his friends. And thus, a little later—for Dickens came and went to France—did he walk the streets of Paris one winter night, his eyes filled

CHARLES DICKENS as CAPTAIN BOBADIL

(*From a Sketch by Thackeray*)

with tears for the death of little Paul Dombey, scarce conscious of where he was.

It was after his return from his first big tour that Dickens made his somewhat formal entry into daily journalism and his somewhat comic exit out of it. Sponsored by a thousand friends and backed by a hundred thousand pounds he assumed the editorial chair of the *Daily Mail* (January 21, 1846), announcing the immediate reform of all England. He was out of the chair in a fit of temper on February 9th. Dickens couldn't work in harness. To daily journalism he never went back. When he took up editing again—in his magazines *Household Words* and *All the Year Round*—he had to be editor, manager and proprietor, all in one.

But in contrast to the disillusionment of his daily journalism were the pleasure and success of the private theatricals which from now till his home broke and the ashes died on the hearth filled a large part of his life. His amateur plays were put on in various theatres and halls, for various charities. Dickens cared little what charity he acted for, so they let him act. One sumptuous occasion was organized at Devonshire House, by the Duke of Devonshire, and graced by the presence of the young Queen and the Prince Consort. Later on, when he took a fine town residence, Tavistock House, Dickens had one of the rooms transformed into a little theatre. Therein were great doings every "Twelfth Night"—his eldest son's birthday. So ran the years, merry with chimes and carols and with the multiplying patter of little feet on the stairs. Later it was all to end in fever, fret and desolation and the ashes to burn dead on the hearth. But as yet it was high noon in Dickens's life—and like Scrooge at his open window he still called to a glad world.

"A CHRISTMAS CAROL": SCROOGE OPENS THE WINDOWS OF HIS SOUL

Yes! and the bedpost was his own. The bed was his own, the room was his own. Best and happiest of all, the Time before him was his own, to make amends in!

"I will live in the Past, the Present, and the Future!" Scrooge repeated, as he scrambled out of bed. "The Spirits of all Three shall strive within me. Oh Jacob Marley! Heaven, and the Christmas Time be praised for this! I say it on my knees, old Jacob, on my knees!"

He was so fluttered and so glowing with his good intentions, that his broken voice would scarcely answer to his call. He had been sobbing violently in his conflict with the Spirit, and his face was wet with tears.

"They are not torn down," cried Scrooge, folding one of his bed-curtains in his arms, "they are not torn down, rings and all. They are here—I am here—the shadows of the things that would have been, may be dispelled. They will be. I know they will!"

His hands were busy with his garments all this time; turning them inside out, putting them on upside down, tearing them, mislaying them, making them parties to every kind of extravagance.

"I don't know what to do!" cried Scrooge, laughing and crying in the same breath; and making a perfect Laocoön of himself with his stockings. "I am as light as a feather, I am as happy as an angel, I am as merry as a schoolboy. I am as giddy as a drunken man. A merry Christmas to everybody! A happy New Year to all the world! Hallo here! Whoop! Hallo!"

He had frisked into the sitting-room, and was now standing there: perfectly winded.

"There's the saucepan that the gruel was in!" cried Scrooge, starting off again, and going round the fireplace. "There's the door, by which the Ghost of Jacob Marley entered! There's the corner where the Ghost of Christmas Present sat! There's the window where I saw the wandering Spirits! It's all right, it's all true, it all happened. Ha ha ha!"

Really, for a man who had been out of practice for so many years, it was a splendid laugh, a most illustrious laugh. The father of a long, long line of brilliant laughs!

"I don't know what day of the month it is!" said Scrooge. "I don't know how long I've been among the Spirits. I don't know anything. I'm quite a baby. Never mind. I don't care. I'd rather be a baby. Hallo! Whoop! Hallo here!"

He was checked in his transports by the churches ringing out the lustiest peals he had ever heard. Clash, clang, hammer; ding, dong, bell. Bell, dong, ding; hammer, clang, clash! Oh, glorious, glorious!

Running to the window, he opened it, and put out his head. No fog, no mist; clear, bright, jovial, stirring, cold; cold, piping for the blood to dance to; Golden sunlight; Heavenly sky; sweet fresh air; merry bells. Oh, glorious! Glorious!

"What's to-day?" cried Scrooge, calling downward to a boy in Sunday clothes, who perhaps had loitered in to look about him.

"Eh?" returned the boy, with all his might of wonder.

"What's to-day, my fine fellow?" said Scrooge.

"To-day!" replied the boy. "Why, CHRISTMAS DAY."

"It's Christmas Day!" said Scrooge to himself. "I haven't missed it. The Spirits have done it all in one night. They can do anything they like. Of course they can. Of course they can. Hallo, my fine fellow!"

"Hallo!" returned the boy.

"Do you know the Poulterer's, in the next street but one, at the corner?" Scrooge inquired.

"I should hope I did," replied the lad.

"An intelligent boy!" said Scrooge. "A remarkable boy! Do you know whether they've sold the prize Turkey that was hanging up there?—Not the little prize Turkey: the big one?"

"What, the one as big as me?" returned the boy.

"What a delightful boy!" said Scrooge. "It's a pleasure to talk to him. Yes, my buck!"

"It's hanging there now," replied the boy.

"Is it?" said Scrooge. "Go and buy it."

"Walk-ER!" exclaimed the boy.

"No, no," said Scrooge, "I am in earnest. Go and buy it, and tell 'em to bring it here, that I may give them the direction where to take it. Come back with the man, and I'll give you a shilling. Come back with him in less than five minutes and I'll give you half-a-crown!"

The boy was off like a shot. He must have had a steady hand at a trigger who could have got a shot off half so fast.

"I'll send it to Bob Cratchit's!" whispered Scrooge, rubbing his hands, and splitting with a laugh. "He shan't know who sends it. It's twice the size of Tiny Tim. Joe Miller never made such a joke as sending it to Bob's will be!"

The hand in which he wrote the address was not a steady one, but write it he did, somehow, and went down-stairs to open the street door, ready for the coming of the poulterer's man. As he stood there, waiting his arrival, the knocker caught his eye.

"I shall love it, as long as I live!" cried Scrooge, patting it with his hand. "I scarcely ever looked at it before. What an honest expression it has in its face! It's a wonderful knocker!—Here's the Turkey. Hallo! Whoop! How are you! Merry Christmas!"

It *was* a Turkey! He never could have stood upon his legs, that bird. He would have snapped 'em short off in a minute, like sticks of sealing-wax.

"Why, it's impossible to carry that to Camden Town," said Scrooge. "You must have a cab."

The chuckle with which he said this, and the chuckle with which he paid for the Turkey, and the chuckle with which he paid for the cab, and the chuckle with which he recompensed the boy, were only to be exceeded by the chuckle with which he sat down breathless in his chair again, and chuckled till he cried.

Shaving was not an easy task, for his hand continued to shake very much; and shaving requires attention, even when you don't dance while you are at it. But if he had cut the end of his nose off, he would have put a piece of sticking-plaister over it, and been quite satisfied.

He dressed himself "all in his best," and at last got out into the streets. The people were by this time pouring forth, as he had seen them with the Ghost of Christmas Present; and walking with his hands behind him, Scrooge regarded every one with a delighted smile. He looked so irresistibly pleasant, in a word, that three or four good-humoured fellows said, "Good morning, sir! A merry Christmas to you!" And Scrooge said often afterwards, that of all the blithe sounds he had ever heard, those were the blithest in his ears.

He had not gone far, when coming on towards him he beheld the portly gentleman, who had walked into his counting-house the day before, and said, "Scrooge and Marley's, I believe?" It sent a pang across his heart to think how this old gentleman would look upon him when they met; but he knew what path lay straight before him, and he took it.

"My dear sir," said Scrooge, quickening his pace, and taking the old gentleman by both his hands. "How do you do? I hope you succeeded yesterday. It was very kind of you. A merry Christmas to you, sir!"

"Mr. Scrooge?"

"Yes," said Scrooge. "That is my name, and I fear it may not be pleasant to you. Allow me to ask your pardon. And will you have the goodness"—here Scrooge whispered in his ear.

"Lord bless me!" cried the gentleman, as if his breath were taken away. "My dear Mr. Scrooge, are you serious?"

"If you please," said Scrooge. "Not a farthing less. A great many back-payments are included in it, I assure you. Will you do me that favour?"

"My dear sir," said the other, shaking hands with him. "I don't know what to say to such munifi——"

"Don't say anything, please," retorted Scrooge. "Come and see me. Will you come and see me?"

"I will!" cried the old gentleman. And it was clear he meant to do it.

"Thank'ee," said Scrooge. "I am much obliged to you. I thank you fifty times. Bless you!"

He went to church, and walked about the streets, and watched the people hurrying to and fro, and patted children on the head, and questioned beggars, and looked down into the kitchens of houses, and up to the windows, and found that everything could yield him pleasure. He had never dreamed that any walk—that anything—could give him so much happiness. In the afternoon he turned his steps towards his nephew's house.

He passed the door a dozen times, before he had the

courage to go up and knock. But he made a dash, and did it.

"Is your master at home, my dear?" said Scrooge to the girl. Nice girl! Very.

"Yes, sir."

"Where is he, my love?" said Scrooge.

"He's in the dining-room, sir, along with mistress. I'll show you up-stairs, if you please."

"Thank'ee. He knows me," said Scrooge, with his hand already on the dining-room lock. "I'll go in here, my dear."

He turned it gently, and sidled his face in, round the door. They were looking at the table (which was spread out in great array); for these young housekeepers are always nervous on such points, and like to see that everything is right.

"Fred!" said Scrooge.

Dear heart alive, how his niece by marriage started! Scrooge had forgotten, for the moment, about her sitting in the corner with the footstool, or he wouldn't have done it, on any account.

"Why bless my soul!" cried Fred, "who's that?"

"It's I. Your uncle Scrooge. I have come to dinner. Will you let me in, Fred?"

Let him in! It is a mercy he didn't shake his arm off. He was at home in five minutes. Nothing could be heartier. His niece looked just the same. So did Topper when *he* came. So did the plump sister when *she* came. So did every one when *they* came. Wonderful party, wonderful games, wonderful unanimity, won-der-ful happiness!

But he was early at the office next morning. Oh, he was early there. If he could only be there first, and catch Bob Cratchit coming late! That was the thing he had set his heart upon.

And he did; yes, he did! The clock struck nine. No Bob. A quarter past. No Bob. He was full eighteen minutes and a half behind his time. Scrooge sat with his door wide open, that he might see him come into the Tank.

His hat was off, before he opened the door; his comforter too. He was on his stool in a jiffy; driving away with his pen, as if he were trying to overtake nine o'clock.

"Hallo!" growled Scrooge, in his accustomed voice, as near as he could feign it. "What do you mean by coming here at this time of day?"

"I am very sorry, sir," said Bob. "I *am* behind my time."

"You are?" repeated Scrooge. "Yes. I think you are. Step this way, sir, if you please."

"It's only once a year, sir," pleaded Bob, appearing from the Tank. "It shall not be repeated. I was making rather merry yesterday, sir."

"Now, I'll tell you what, my friend," said Scrooge, "I am not going to stand this sort of thing any longer. And therefore," he continued, leaping from his stool, and giving Bob such a dig in the waistcoat that he staggered back into the Tank again; "and therefore I am about to raise your salary!"

Bob trembled, and got a little nearer to the ruler. He had a momentary idea of knocking Scrooge down with it, holding him, and calling to the people in the court for help and a strait-waistcoat.

"A merry Christmas, Bob!" said Scrooge, with an earnestness that could not be mistaken, as he clapped him on the back. "A merrier Christmas, Bob, my good fellow, than I have given you for many a year! I'll raise your salary, and endeavour to assist your struggling family, and we will discuss your affairs this very afternoon, over a Christmas bowl of smoking bishop, Bob! Make up the fires, and buy another coal-scuttle before you dot another i, Bob Cratchit!"

Scrooge was better than his word. He did it all, and infinitely more; and to Tiny Tim, who did NOT die, he was a second father. He became as good a friend, as good a master, and as good a man, as the good old city knew, or any other good old city, town, or borough, in the good old world. Some people laughed to see the alteration in him, but he let them laugh, and little heeded them; for he was wise enough to know that nothing ever happened on this globe, for good, at which some people did not have their fill of laughter in the outset; and knowing that such as these would be blind anyway, he thought it quite as well that they should wrinkle up their eyes in grins, as have the malady in less attractive forms. His own heart laughed; and that was quite enough for him.

He had no further intercourse with Spirits, but lived upon the Total Abstinence Principle, ever afterwards; and it was always said of him, that he knew how to keep Christmas well, if any man alive possessed the knowledge. May that be truly said of us, and all of us! And so, as Tiny Tim observed, God bless Us, Every One!

THE FLOOD TIDE OF SUCCESS
1846–1850

Chapter Six

THE FLOOD TIDE OF SUCCESS
1846–1850

THE YEARS that elapsed between Dickens's return from Europe and the publication of the book, *David Copperfield*, may be said to mark the highest reach of his mature genius and the pinnacle of his fame. His popularity, it is true, never declined. It is true also that it was after this period that he developed and revealed to the world the marvellous talent for the public rendering of his written pages which was to enthrall England and America. Yet he never again enjoyed in so full a measure as now the unbounded energy of working power, the exuberant fertility of genius. After this period there is an increasing strain of overwork, a wear and tear of domestic infelicity, a restlessness of the soul—dare one say, a sense of guilt—which chafed and impeded the mechanism of his brilliant intellect and in the end shattered it in disaster.

Dickens brought back with him from the Continent the notes which began his *Pictures from Italy*. They are of little interest now except to illustrate his own character. To the European political situation, the ground swell that preceded the great upheaval of 1848, his senses made no response. For the historic past he had no education: for the immediate past no sympathy. All about him was still the wreckage of the Napoleonic Empire, the old soldiers of Austerlitz and Jena. He saw nothing but toothless old men with funny red ribbons. Later on he was to be in America just after the mighty epic of the Civil War, and to hear there nothing but his own voice. His *Pictures* are merely picturesque, at times comic, jottings of people and things, with here and there a vision of a public execution or a torture chamber. Dickens always had a fine taste in horrors.

But far above the pictures and placed by some readers among his greatest work was the book *Dombey and Son,* written in this period (in part in Paris), and published as a book in 1848. The death of little Paul Dombey is as famous in literature as that of Little Nell. For fifty years there was sung at Victorian pianos the beautiful melody, "What are the wild waves saying, sister, the whole day long?"—the questioning of little Paul, to whom already, fading beside the sea, the angels were calling in the murmur of the waves. But, as with Little Nell, for most of us today, the theme is too harrowing. We no longer revel in the sheer luxury of sorrow as did the readers of Dickens's day, even the highest among them. "I have cried and sobbed over it last night and again and again this morning," wrote

Lord Jeffrey, "and felt my heart purified by those tears, and blessed you for making me shed them."

Dombey and Son was followed by *The Haunted Man*, sold and first published in America, a new flight of Dickens's enterprise. The publication of the *American Notes* and *Martin Chuzzlewit* had called forth bitter denunciation of Dickens in America. But the busy public of those roaring days had extended to him an easy-going forgiveness; after all, he had only called them crooks: he hadn't denied their smartness. If he had classed them in with the Bumbles and the Deadlocks and the Willets, that would have been another thing. *The Haunted Man* was a big success on both sides of the Atlantic and presently on the stage. Few of us would read it today. Victorian spectres with "an awful voice," and apparitions which call, "Forbear!" have been put out of commission by the "talkies." All that apparatus is today mere litter. Mrs. Crowes' *Night Thoughts*—the Victorian acme of terror—would with us put a child to sleep in the day.

But the great book was to follow. *David Copperfield* was begun in 1848; it ran in monthly parts in 1848 and 1849, and was issued in 1850 as a book, illustrated like all the works since Pickwick by the droll pencil of "Phiz," otherwise, Hablôt Browne. It was, and has remained ever since, an overwhelming success. Leaving aside *Pickwick*, it has been the most acclaimed of Dickens's books. *Pickwick* stands all by itself: its unique origin defied repetition. Like youth itself it could only come once. Not being so much a book as a world, it cannot be compared. Apart from that, *David Copperfield* has the front place. Dickens himself said that like all fathers he had a favourite child and his name was David Copperfield. In this there is an eternal truth. For the story in its opening and origin reflects the misery of Dickens's own childhood. He had planned an autobiography. He found it too poignant to write. So to David is transferred the tragic drudgery of little Dickens, ten years old, in his garret and workshop.

But the sorrows of David's early life are soon forgotten in the interest of what follows. This is not for David's own sake. He is only a sort of abstraction or looking glass. But in the glass we see Micawber and Uriah Heep and other immortals. Above all we see it reflect all the colours of the morning when David falls in love with Dora Spenlow: here is love as it was, or was depicted, in the mid-Victorian days—devoted, ecstatic and exalted—before it gave way to the tawdry "sex-appeal" which is replacing it in our life and literature. Let the reader float to the clouds in its soft atmosphere. In the passages that follow—beyond the indication that the bitter old maid, Miss Murdstone, had played a cruel part in David's youth—the reader needs neither comment nor explanation.

THE WINGS OF THE MORNING: DAVID COPPERFIELD FALLS IN LOVE

THERE WAS a lovely garden to Mr. Spenlow's house; and though that was not the best time of the year for seeing a garden, it was beautifully kept, that I was quite enchanted. There was a charming lawn, there were clusters of trees, and there were perspective walks that I could just distinguish in the dark, arched over with trellis-work, on which shrubs and flowers grew in the growing season. "Here Miss Spenlow walks by herself," I thought. "Dear me!"

We went into the house, which was cheerfully lighted up, and into a hall where there were all sorts of hats, caps, greatcoats, plaids, gloves, whips, and walking-sticks. "Where is Miss Dora?" said Mr. Spenlow to the servant. "Dora!" I thought. "What a beautiful name!"

We turned into a room near at hand (I think it was the identical breakfast-room, made memorable by the brown East Indian Sherry), and I heard a voice say, "Mr. Copperfield, my daughter Dora, and my daughter Dora's confidential friend!" It was, no doubt, Mr. Spenlow's voice, but I didn't know it, and I didn't care whose it was. All was over in a moment. I had fulfilled my destiny. I was a captive and a slave. I loved Dora Spenlow to distraction!

She was more than human to me. She was a Fairy,

a Sylph, I don't know what she was—anything that no one ever saw, and everything that everybody ever wanted. I was swallowed up in an abyss of love in an instant. There was no pausing on the brink; no looking down, or looking back; I was gone, headlong, before I had sense to say a word to her.

"*I,*" observed a well-remembered voice, when I had bowed and murmured something, "have seen Mr. Copperfield before." The speaker was not Dora. No; the confidential friend, Miss Murdstone!

I don't think I was much astonished. To the best of my judgment, no capacity of astonishment was left in me. There was nothing worth mentioning in the material world, but Dora Spenlow, to be astonished about. I said, "How do you do, Miss Murdstone? I hope you are well." She answered, "Very well." I said, "How is Mr. Murdstone?" She replied, "My brother is robust, I am obliged to you."

Mr. Spenlow, who, I suppose, had been surprised to see us recognise each other, then put in his word.

"I am glad to find," he said, "Copperfield, that you and Miss Murdstone are already acquainted."

"Mr. Copperfield and myself," said Miss Murdstone, with severe composure, "are connections. We were once slightly acquainted. It was in his childish days. Circumstances have separated us since. I should not have known him."

I replied that I should have known her, anywhere. Which was true enough.

I FALL INTO CAPTIVITY

From an engraving by *Phiz*.

"Miss Murdstone has had the goodness," said Mr. Spenlow to me, "to accept the office—if I may so describe it—of my daughter Dora's confidential friend. My daughter Dora having, unhappily, no mother, Miss Murdstone is obliging enough to become her companion and protector."

A passing thought occurred to me that Miss Murdstone, like the pocket instrument called a life-preserver, was not so much designed for purposes of protection as of assault. But as I had none but passing thoughts for any subject save Dora, I glanced at her, directly afterwards, and was thinking that I saw, in her prettily pettish manner, that she was not very much inclined to be particularly confidential to her companion and protector, when a bell rang, which Mr. Spenlow said was the first dinner-bell, and so carried me off to dress.

The idea of dressing one's self, or doing anything in the way of action, in that state of love, was a little too ridiculous. I could only sit down before my fire, biting the key of my carpet-bag, and think of the captivating, girlish, bright-eyed, lovely Dora. What a form she had, what a face she had, what a graceful, variable, enchanting manner!

The bell rang again so soon that I made a mere scramble of my dressing, instead of the careful operation I could have wished under the circumstances, and went downstairs. There was some company. Dora was talking to an old gentleman with a gray head. Gray as he was

—and a great-grandfather into the bargain, for he said so—I was madly jealous of him.

What a state of mind I was in! I was jealous of everybody. I couldn't bear the idea of anybody knowing Mr. Spenlow better than I did. It was torturing to me to hear them talk of occurrences in which I had had no share. When a most amiable person, with a highly polished bald head, asked me across the dinner-table, if that were the first occasion of my seeing the grounds, I could have done anything to him that was savage and revengeful.

I don't remember who was there, except Dora. I have not the least idea what we had for dinner, besides Dora. My impression is, that I dined off Dora, entirely, and sent away half a dozen plates untouched. I sat next to her. I talked to her. She had the most delightful little voice, the gayest little laugh, the pleasantest and most fascinating little ways, that ever led a lost youth into hopeless slavery. She was rather diminutive altogether. So much the more precious, I thought.

*   *   *   *   *

All I know of the rest of the evening is, that I heard the empress of my heart sing enchanted ballads in the French language, generally to the effect that, whatever was the matter, we ought always to dance. Ta ra la, Ta ra la! accompanying herself on a glorified instrument, resembling a guitar. That I was lost in blissful delirium. That I refused refreshment. That my soul recoiled from punch particularly. That when Miss

Murdstone took her into custody, and led her away, she smiled, and give me her delicious hand. That I caught a view of myself in a mirror, looking perfectly imbecile and idiotic. That I retired to bed in a most maudlin state of mind, and got up in a crisis of feeble infatuation.

It was a fine morning, and early, and I thought I would go and take a stroll down one of those wire-arched walks, and indulge my passion by dwelling on her image. On my way through the hall, I encountered her little dog, who was called Jip—short for Gipsy. I approached him tenderly, for I loved even him; but he showed his whole set of teeth, got under a chair expressly to snarl, and wouldn't hear of the least familiarity.

The garden was cool and solitary. I walked about, wondering what my feelings of happiness would be, if I could ever become engaged to this dear wonder. As to marriage, and fortune, and all that, I believe I was almost as innocently undesigning then, as when I loved little Em'ly. To be allowed to call her "Dora," to write to her, to dote upon and worship her, to have reason to think that when she was with other people she was yet mindful of me, seemed to me the summit of human ambition—I am sure it was the summit of mine. There is no doubt whatever that I was a lackadaisical young spooney; but there was a purity of heart in all this still, that prevents my having quite a contemptuous recollection of it, let me laugh as I may.

*   *   *   *   *

We departed early in the morning, for we had a Salvage case coming on in the Admiralty Court, requiring a rather accurate knowledge of the whole science of navigation, in which (as we couldn't be expected to know much about those matters in the Commons) the judge had entreated two old Trinity Masters, for charity's sake, to come and help him out. Dora was at the breakfast-table to make the tea again, however; and I had the melancholy pleasure of taking off my hat to her in the phaeton, as she stood on the door-step with Jip in her arms.

What the Admiralty was to me that day; what nonsense I made of our case in my mind, as I listened to it; how I saw "DORA" engraved upon the blade of the silver oar which they lay upon the table, as the emblem of that high jurisdiction; and how I felt, when Mr. Spenlow went home without me (I had had an insane hope that he might take me back again), as if I were a mariner myself, and the ship to which I belonged had sailed away and left me on a desert island; I shall make no fruitless effort to describe. If that sleepy old court could rouse itself, and present in any visible form the day-dreams I have had in it about Dora, it would reveal my truth.

I don't mean the dreams that I dreamed on that day alone, but day after day, from week to week, and term to term. I went there, not to attend to what was going on, but to think about Dora. If I ever bestowed a thought upon the cases, as they dragged their slow length before me, it was only to wonder, in the matrimonial cases (remembering Dora), how it was that married people could ever be otherwise than happy; and, in the prerogative cases, to consider, if the money in question had been left to me, what were the foremost steps I should immediately have taken in regard to Dora. Within the first week of my passion, I bought four sumptuous waistcoats—not for myself; *I* had no pride in them; for Dora—and took to wearing straw-coloured kid gloves in the streets, and laid the foundations of all the corns I have ever had. If the boots I wore at that period could only be produced and compared with the natural size of my feet, they would show what the state of my heart was, in a most affecting manner.

DICKENS REFORMS THE WORLD
1850–1854

Chapter Seven

DICKENS REFORMS THE WORLD
1850–1854

As DICKENS passed into middle life—old age he never reached—his writing took on more and more an element of social purpose. In his earliest work he had written as a bird sings, without aim, without purpose, without pay. But even with Pickwick there begins at least the idea of the exaltations of goodness and the vision of the meek inheriting the earth. With *Oliver* and *Nicholas Nickleby* the theme is carried further. We see sin being cast in the persons of Bumble and Squeers. As the years went on and Dickens's place and popularity grew, he felt himself more and more in the position of a custodian of national morals. This was all the easier for him in that his ideas were entirely "respectable" and "Victorian." Even if he didn't believe in dull tones and stupid squires, at least he thoroughly believed in property, money and the established order of things. He had no communism to advocate like his contemporary, Karl Marx, no land to confiscate like Henry George, no God and Bible to denounce like Mark Twain behind

145

his gag. Dickens's social reform means the insistence on charity to all men, aid to the poor, honesty and integrity—not a system but a spirit. It contained much general invective against parliament without any exact indication of what parliament was to do.

It was this eagerness to be a moral guide which had seated him in his editorial chair. It was in this spirit, just at this phase of his life, that he put together his *Child's History of England* and his *Life of Our Lord*. These especially were for his own children. His charity began at home.

He wrote for his children a history of England (1851), in some respects an admirable book, vivid and earnest and not afraid of truth. Henry VIII appears as a "blot of blood and grease upon the history of England." But in its proportion the book is all upside down, all Druids and Saxons with modern history telescoped to one brief chapter. It is marred by Dickens's love of horrors. The burning of Bishop Hooper is cruel reading for a little child. But Dickens had already gone further than profane history. He undertook (1849) to rewrite, for his children alone, the narrative of the New Testament. This was not printed till the death of his last surviving child (Sir Henry Fielding Dickens) who permitted its publication (1934). It satisfied a wide initial curiosity but is of no lasting value. Not even Charles Dickens could improve the marvellous language of King James translations, hallowed by these hundred years; not even Charles Dickens could replace with

CHARLES DICKENS and the COALHEAVER'S CHILD
(Etched by Pailthorpe)

other words the chapters and the verses that for three hundred years, on land and sea, at the pulpit, at the altar and the deathbed had been the treasured heritage of our race. Not even Dickens could reëdit Jesus Christ.

It was this same "urge" that led Dickens to undertake the editorship (1850) of a new weekly journal, *Household Words*, planned and designed by himself and dominated by his ideas. The contributors—whose work Dickens "edited" to the top of his bent—did not even sign their names. "All," he said, "will seem to express the general mind and purpose of the journal which is the raising up of those that are down and the general improvement of our social condition." Dickens's editorial labours, arduous and minute, on this periodical and its successor ended only at his death. But Dickens's passion for bettering the world found a noble outlet in his novel *Bleak House*, which began serial publication in 1852. Here indeed is a wonderful book: the details of the personal plot may be, as usual with Dickens, intricate and improbable, but the theme in the background—the law's delay, the tragedies of chancery—is as sombre and as sustained as that of a Greek tragedy. The presentation of the fictitious lawsuit of Jarndyce *vs.* Jarndyce, which had worn away the liver of two generations of unhappy suitors, was no whit exaggerated beyond the existing situation of the English court of chancery. The book helped enormously towards the reform of the law. Its opening picture of the fog falling over Lincoln's Inn—emblem and symbol of the darkness of the law—stands unforgettable.

But Dickens had the artistic sense not to leave his plea for social reform unrelieved by a contrasting element. In opposition to real social betterment appear the heroic efforts of Mrs. Jellaby on behalf of the natives of Borioboola-Gha, and those of Mrs. Pardiggle on whose unhappy children are levied forced contributions to their mother's "Bands of Joy" and such activities. Thus did Dickens keep his righteousness from becoming maudlin.

"BLEAK HOUSE": THE FOG FALLS OVER LINCOLN'S INN . . . AND LIFTS OVER BORIOBOOLA-GHA

LONDON. Michaelmas Term lately over, and the Lord Chancellor sitting in Lincoln's Inn Hall. Implacable November weather. As much mud in the streets, as if the waters had but newly retired from the face of the earth, and it would not be wonderful to meet a Megalosaurus, forty feet long or so, waddling like an elephantine lizard up Holborn Hill. Smoke lowering down from chimney-pots, making a soft black drizzle, with flakes of soot in it as big as full-grown snow-flakes —gone into mourning, one might imagine, for the death of the sun. Dogs, undistinguishable in mire. Horses, scarcely better; splashed to their very blinkers. Foot passengers, jostling one another's umbrellas, in a general infection of ill-temper, and losing their foothold at street-corners, where tens of thousands of other foot passengers have been slipping and sliding since the day broke (if this day ever broke), adding new deposits to the crust upon crust of mud, sticking at those points tenaciously to the pavement, and accumulating at compound interest.

Fog everywhere. Fog up the river, where it flows among green aits and meadows; fog down the river, where it rolls defiled among the tiers of shipping, and the waterside pollutions of a great (and dirty) city. Fog on the Essex marshes, fog on the Kentish heights. Fog creeping into the cabooses of collier-brigs, fog lying out on the yards, and hovering in the rigging of great ships; fog drooping on the gunwales of barges and small boats. Fog in the eyes and throats of ancient Greenwich pensioners, wheezing by the firesides of their wards; fog in the stem and bowl of the afternoon pipe of the wrathful skipper, down in his close cabin; fog cruelly pinching the toes and fingers of his shivering little 'prentice boy on deck. Chance people on the bridges peeping over the parapets into a nether sky of fog, with fog all round them, as if they were up in a balloon, and hanging in the misty clouds.

Gas looming through the fog in divers places in the streets, much as the sun may, from the spongy fields, be seen to loom by husbandman and ploughboy. Most of the shops lighted two hours before their time—as the gas seems to know, for it has a haggard and unwilling look.

The raw afternoon is rawest, and the dense fog is densest, and the muddy streets are muddiest, near that leaden-headed old obstruction, appropriate ornament for the threshold of a leaden-headed old corporation: Temple Bar. And hard by Temple Bar, in Lincoln's Inn Hall, at the very heart of the fog, sits the Lord High Chancellor in his High Court of Chancery.

Never can there come fog too thick, never can there come mud and mire too deep, to assort with the groping and floundering condition which this High Court of Chancery, most pestilent of hoary sinners, holds, this day, in the sight of heaven and earth.

On such an afternoon, if ever, the Lord High Chancellor ought to be sitting here—as here he is—with a foggy glory round his head, softly fenced in with crimson cloth and curtains, addressed by a large advocate with great whiskers, a little voice, and an interminable brief, and outwardly directing his contemplation to the lantern in the roof, where he can see nothing but fog. On such an afternoon, some score of members of the High Court of Chancery bar ought to be—as here they are—mistily engaged in one of the ten thousand stages of an endless cause, tripping one another up on slippery precedents, groping knee-deep in technicalities, running their goat-hair and horse-hair warded heads against walls of words, and making a pretence of equity with serious faces, as players might. On such an afternoon, the various solicitors in the cause, some two or three of whom have inherited it from their fathers, who made a fortune by it, ought to be—as are they not?— ranged in a line, in a long matted well (but you might look in vain for Truth at the bottom of it), between the registrar's red table and the silk gowns, with bills, cross-bills, answers, rejoinders, injunctions, affidavits, issues, references to masters, masters' reports, mountains of costly nonsense, piled before them. Well may the court be dim, with wasting candles here and there; well may the fog hang heavy in it, as if it would never get out; well may the stained glass windows lose their colour, and admit no light of day into the place; well may the uninitiated from the streets, who peep in through the glass panes in the door, be deterred from entrance by its owlish aspect, and by the drawl languidly echoing to the roof from the padded dais where the Lord High Chancellor looks into the lantern that has no light in it, and where the attendant wigs are all stuck in a fog-bank! This is the Court of Chancery; which has its decaying houses and its blighted lands in every shire; which has its worn-out lunatic in every madhouse, and its dead in every churchyard; which has its ruined suitor, with his slipshod heels and threadbare dress, borrowing and begging through the round of every man's acquaintance; which gives to monied might, the means abundantly of wearying out the right; which so exhausts finances, patience, courage, hope; so overthrows the brain and breaks the heart; that there is not an honourable man among its practitioners who would not give—who does not often give the warning, "Suffer any wrong that can be done you, rather than come here!"

Who happen to be in the Lord Chancellor's court this murky afternoon besides the Lord Chancellor, the counsel in the cause, two or three counsel who are never in any cause, and the well of solicitors before mentioned? There is the registrar below the Judge, in wig and gown; and there are two or three maces, or pettybags, or privy purses, or whatever they may be, in

legal court suits. These are all yawning; for no crumb
of amusement ever falls from JARNDYCE AND JARNDYCE
(the cause in hand), which was squeezed dry years upon
years ago. The short-hand writers, the reporters of the
court, and the reporters of the newspapers, invariably
decamp with the rest of the regulars when Jarndyce
and Jarndyce comes on. Their places are a blank.
Standing on a seat at the side of the hall, the better
to peer into the curtained sanctuary, is a little mad
old woman in a squeezed bonnet, who is always in
court, from its sitting to its rising, and always expecting some incomprehensible judgment to be given in her
favour. Some say she really is, or was, a party to a suit;
but no one knows for certain because, no one cares.
She carries some small litter in her reticule which she
calls her documents; principally consisting of paper
matches and dry lavender. A sallow prisoner has come
up, in custody, for the half-dozenth time, to make a
personal application "to purge himself of his contempt"; which, being a solitary surviving executor who
has fallen into a state of conglomeration about accounts of which it is not pretended that he had ever
any knowledge, he is not at all likely ever to do. In the
meantime his prospects in life are ended. Another
ruined suitor, who periodically appears from Shropshire, and breaks out into efforts to address the Chancellor at the close of the day's business, and who can
by no means be made to understand that the Chancellor is legally ignorant of his existence after making

it desolate for a quarter of a century, plants himself in a good place and keeps an eye on the Judge, ready to call out "My Lord!" in a voice of sonorous complaint, on the instant of his rising. A few lawyers' clerks and others who know this suitor by sight, linger, on the chance of his furnishing some fun, and enlivening the dismal weather a little.

Jarndyce and Jarndyce drones on. This scarecrow of a suit has, in course of time, become so complicated, that no man alive knows what it means. The parties to it understand it least; but it has been observed that no two Chancery lawyers can talk about it for five minutes, without coming to a total disagreement as to all the premises. Innumerable children have been born into the cause; innumerable young people have married into it; innumerable old people have died out of it. Scores of persons have deliriously found themselves made parties in Jarndyce and Jarndyce, without knowing how or why; whole families have inherited legendary hatreds with the suit. The little plaintiff or defendant, who was promised a new rocking-horse when Jarndyce and Jarndyce should be settled, has grown up, possessed himself of a real horse, and trotted away into the other world. Fair wards of court have faded into mothers and grandmothers; a long procession of Chancellors has come in and gone out; the legion of bills in the suit have been transformed into mere bills of mortality; there are not three Jarndyces left upon the earth perhaps, since old Tom Jarndyce in

despair blew his brains out at a coffee-house in Chancery
Lane; but Jarndyce and Jarndyce still drags its dreary
length before the Court, perennially hopeless.

Jarndyce and Jarndyce has passed into a joke. That
is the only good that has ever come of it. It has been
death to many, but it is a joke in the profession. Every
master in Chancery has had a reference out of it. Every
Chancellor was "in it," for somebody or other, when he
was counsel at the bar. Good things have been said
about it by blue-nosed, bulbous-shoed old benchers, in
select port-wine committee after dinner in hall. Articled clerks have been in the habit of fleshing their legal
wit upon it. The last Lord Chancellor handled it neatly
when, correcting Mr. Blowers, the eminent silk gown
who said that such a thing might happen when the
sky rained potatoes, he observed, "or when we get
through Jarndyce and Jarndyce, Mr. Blowers;"—a
pleasantry that particularly tickled the maces, bags,
and purses.

How many people out of the suit, Jarndyce and
Jarndyce has stretched forth its unwholesome hand
to spoil and corrupt, would be a very wide question.
From the master, upon whose impaling files reams of
dusty warrants in Jarndyce and Jarndyce have grimly
writhed into many shapes; down to the copying-clerk
in the Six Clerks' Office, who has copied his tens of
thousands of Chancery-folio-pages under that eternal
heading; no man's nature has been made better by it.
In trickery, evasion, procrastination, spoliation, bother-

ation, under false pretences of all sorts, there are influences that can never come to good. The very solicitors' boys who have kept the wretched suitors at bay, by protesting time out of mind that Mr. Chizzle, Mizzle, or otherwise, was particularly engaged and had appointments until dinner, may have got an extra moral twist and shuffle into themselves out of Jarndyce and Jarndyce. The receiver in the cause has acquired a goodly sum of money by it, but has acquired too a distrust of his own mother, and a contempt for his own kind. Chizzle, Mizzle, and otherwise, have lapsed into a habit of vaguely promising themselves that they will look into that outstanding little matter, and see what can be done for Drizzle—who was not well used—when Jarndyce and Jarndyce shall be got out of the office. Shirking and sharking, in all their many varieties, have been sown broadcast by the ill-fated cause; and even those who have contemplated its history from the outermost circle of such evil, have been insensibly tempted into a loose way of letting bad things alone to take their own bad course, and a loose belief that if the world go wrong, it was, in some off-hand manner, never meant to go right.

Thus, in the midst of the mud and at the heart of the fog, sits the Lord High Chancellor in his High Court of Chancery.

"Mr. Tangle," says the Lord High Chancellor, latterly something restless under the eloquence of that learned gentleman.

"Mlud," says Mr. Tangle. Mr. Tangle knows more of Jarndyce and Jarndyce than anybody. He is famous for it—supposed never to have read anything else since he left school.

"Have you nearly concluded your argument?"

"Mlud, no—variety of points—feel it my duty tsubmit—ludship," is the reply that slides out of Mr. Tangle.

"Several members of the bar are still to be heard, I believe?" says the Chancellor, with a slight smile.

Eighteen of Mr. Tangle's learned friends, each armed with a little summary of eighteen hundred sheets, bob up like eighteen hammers in a pianoforte, make eighteen bows, and drop into their eighteen places of obscurity.

"We will proceed with the hearing on Wednesday fortnight," says the Chancellor. For the question at issue is only a question of costs, a mere bud on the forest tree of the parent suit, and really will come to a settlement one of these days.

The Chancellor rises; the bar rises; the prisoner is brought forward in a hurry; the man from Shropshire cries, "My lord!" Maces, bags, and purses, indignantly proclaim silence, and frown at the man from Shropshire.

"In reference," proceeds the Chancellor, still on Jarndyce and Jarndyce, "to the young girl——"

"Begludship's pardon—boy," says Mr. Tangle, prematurely.

"In reference," proceeds the Chancellor, with extra distinctness, "to the young girl and boy, the two young people,"

(Mr. Tangle crushed.)

"Whom I directed to be in attendance to-day, and who are now in my private room, I will see them and satisfy myself as to the expediency of making the order for their residing with their uncle."

Mr. Tangle on his legs again.

"Beguldship's pardon—dead."

"With their," Chancellor looking through his double eyeglass at the papers on his desk, "grandfather."

"Beguldship's pardon—victim of rash action— brains."

Suddenly a very little counsel, with a terrific bass voice, arises, fully inflated, in the back settlements of the fog, and says, "Will your lordship allow me? I appear for him. He is a cousin, several times removed. I am not at the moment prepared to inform the Court in what exact remove he is a cousin; but he *is* a cousin."

Leaving this address (delivered like a sepulchral message) ringing in the rafters of the roof, the very little counsel drops, and the fog knows him no more. Everybody looks for him. Nobody can see him.

"I will speak with both the young people," says the Chancellor anew, "and satisfy myself on the subject of their residing with their cousin. I will mention the matter tomorrow morning when I take my seat."

The Chancellor is about to bow to the bar, when the

prisoner is presented. Nothing can possibly come of the prisoner's conglomeration, but his being sent back to prison; which is soon done. The man from Shropshire ventures another demonstrative "My lord!" but the Chancellor, being aware of him, has dexterously vanished. Everybody else quickly vanishes too. A battery of blue bags is loaded with heavy charges of papers and carried off by clerks; the little mad old woman marches off with her documents; the empty court is locked up. If all the injustice it has committed, and all the misery it has caused, could only be locked up with it, and the whole burnt away in a great funeral pyre,— why so much the better for other parties than the parties in Jarndyce and Jarndyce!

* * * * *

. . . we turned up under an archway to our destination: a narrow street of high houses, like an oblong cistern to hold the fog. There was a confused little crowd of people, principally children, gathered about the house at which we stopped, which had a tarnished brass plate on the door, with the inscription, JELLYBY.

"Don't be frightened!" said Mr. Guppy, looking in at the coach-window. "One of the young Jellybys been and got his head through the area railings!"

"O poor child," said I, "let me out, if you please!"

"Pray be careful of yourself, miss. The young Jellybys are always up to something," said Mr. Guppy.

I made my way to the poor child, who was one of the dirtiest little unfortunates I ever saw, and found

him very hot and frightened, and crying loudly, fixed
by the neck between two iron railings, while a milkman
and a beadle, with the kindest intentions possible, were
endeavouring to drag him back by the legs, under a
general impression that his skull was compressible by
those means. As I found (after pacifying him), that he
was a little boy, with a naturally large head, I thought
that, perhaps, where his head could go, his body could
follow, and mentioned that the best mode of extrica-
tion might be to push him forward. This was so favourably received by the milkman and beadle, that he would
immediately have been pushed into the area, if I had
not held his pinafore, while Richard and Mr. Guppy
ran down through the kitchen, to catch him when he
should be released. At last he was happily got down
without any accident, and then he began to beat Mr.
Guppy with a hoop-stick in quite a frantic manner.

Nobody had appeared belonging to the house, except
a person in pattens, who had been poking at the child
from below with a broom; I don't know with what
object, and I don't think she did. I therefore supposed
that Mrs. Jellyby was not at home; and was quite
surprised when the person appeared in the passage
without the pattens, and going up to the back room
on the first floor, before Ada and me, announced us as,
"Them two young ladies, Missis Jellyby!" We passed
several more children on the way up, whom it was
difficult to avoid treading on in the dark; and as we
came into Mrs. Jellyby's presence, one of the poor

little things fell downstairs—down a whole flight (as it sounded to me), with a great noise.

Mrs. Jellyby, whose face reflected none of the uneasiness which we could not help showing in our own faces, as the dear child's head recorded its passage with a bump on every stair—Richard afterwards said he counted seven, besides one for the landing—received us with perfect equanimity. She was a pretty, very diminutive, plump woman, of from forty to fifty, with handsome eyes, though they had a curious habit of seeming to look a long way off. As if—I am quoting Richard again—they could see nothing nearer than Africa!

"I am very glad indeed," said Mrs. Jellyby, in an agreeable voice, "to have the pleasure of receiving you. I have a great respect for Mr. Jarndyce; and no one in whom he is interested can be an object of indifference to me."

We expressed our acknowledgments, and sat down behind the door where there was a lame invalid of a sofa. Mrs. Jellyby had very good hair, but was too much occupied with her African duties to brush it. The shawl in which she had been loosely muffled, dropped on to her chair when she advanced to us; and as she turned to resume her seat, we could not help noticing that her dress didn't nearly meet up the back, and that the open space was railed across with a lattice-work of stay-lace—like a summer-house.

The room, which was strewn with papers and nearly

filled by a great writing-table covered with similar litter, was, I must say, not only very untidy, but very dirty. We were obliged to take notice of that with our sense of sight, even while, with our sense of hearing, we followed the poor child who had tumbled downstairs: I think into the back kitchen, where somebody seemed to stifle him.

But what principally struck us was a jaded and unhealthy-looking, though by no means plain girl, at the writing-table, who sat biting the feather of her pen, and staring at us. I suppose nobody ever was in such a state of ink. And, from her tumbled hair to her pretty feet, which were disfigured with frayed and broken satin slippers trodden down at heel, she really seemed to have no article of dress upon her, from a pin upwards, that was in its proper condition or its right place.

"You find me, my dears," said Mrs. Jellyby, snuffing the two great office candles in tin candlesticks which made the room taste strongly of hot tallow (the fire had gone out, and there was nothing in the grate but ashes, a bundle of wood, and a poker), "you find me, my dears, as usual, very busy; but that you will excuse. The African project at present employs my whole time. It involves me in correspondence with public bodies, and with private individuals anxious for the welfare of their species all over the country. I am happy to say it is advancing. We hope by this time next year to have from a hundred and fifty to two hundred healthy families cultivating coffee and educating the natives of Borrioboola-Gha, on the left bank of the Niger."

As Ada said nothing, but looked at me, I said it must be very gratifying.

"It *is* gratifying," said Mrs. Jellyby. "It involves the devotion of all my energies, such as they are; but that is nothing, so that it succeeds; and I am more confident of success every day. Do you know, Miss Summerson, I almost wonder that *you* never turned your thoughts to Africa."

This application of the subject was really so unexpected to me, that I was quite at a loss how to receive it. I hinted that the climate——

"The finest climate in the world!" said Mrs. Jellyby.

"Indeed, ma'am?"

"Certainly. With precaution," said Mrs. Jellyby. "You may go into Holborn, without precaution, and be run over. You may go into Holborn, with precaution, and never be run over. Just so with Africa."

I said, "No doubt."—I meant as to Holborn.

"If you would like," said Mrs. Jellyby, putting a number of papers towards us, "to look over some remarks on that head, and on the general subject (which have been extensively circulated), while I finish a letter I am now dictating—to my eldest daughter, who is my amanuensis——"

The girl at the table left off biting her pen, and made a return to our recognition, which was half bashful and half sulky.

"—I shall then have finished for the present," proceeded Mrs. Jellyby, with a sweet smile; "though my work is never done. Where are you, Caddy?"

"'Presents her compliments to Mr. Swallow, and begs——'" said Caddy.

"'And begs,'" said Mrs. Jellyby, dictating, "'to inform him, in reference to his letter of inquiry on the African project.'—No, Peepy! Not on any account!"

Peepy (so self-named) was the unfortunate child who had fallen downstairs, who now interrupted the correspondence by presenting himself, with a strip of plaister on his forehead, to exhibit his wounded knees, in which Ada and I did not know which to pity most—the bruises or the dirt. Mrs. Jellyby merely added, with the serene composure with which she said everything, "Go along, you naughty Peepy!" and fixed her fine eyes on Africa again.

However, as she at once proceeded with her dictation, and as I interrupted nothing by doing it, I ventured quietly to stop poor Peepy as he was going out, and to take him up to nurse. He looked very much astonished at it, and at Ada's kissing him; but soon fell fast asleep in my arms, sobbing at longer and longer intervals, until he was quiet. I was so occupied with Peepy that I lost the letter in detail, though I derived such a general impression from it of the momentous importance of Africa, and the utter insignificance of all other places and things, that I felt quite ashamed to have thought so little about it.

THE FALLING SHADOW OF THE PRISON WALL
1854–1858

Chapter Eight

THE FALLING SHADOW OF THE PRISON WALL
1854–1858

FROM THE WRITING of *Bleak House* Dickens turned the composition of his *Hard Times,* which ran as a serial in 1854 in his new journal. This is meant as another "sweeping denunciation." But it missed its mark and has long since gone into the litter heap. The moral theme is so prominent that it kills the story, the characters becoming as namby-pamby as a copybook. Dickens felt that something was wrong with "free composition" and "liberty," but as he didn't know what it was, he laid it as a personal sin at the door of the manufacturers. Macaulay called the book "sullen socialism." The world soon forgot it.

This period of Dickens's life was enlivened by his pleasant summers in France, spent almost entirely at Boulogne. The French public of the Second Empire had taken Dickens to their heart. His early books had been translated into French in a haphazard way by anybody and everybody. Now, however, Messrs. Hachette engaged a whole staff of translators and brought out a real edition of Dickens. It was a brave attempt and a success. But most of the humour of Dickens is untranslatable. It is too much connected with the misuse of our own language. How can Mr. Weller senior and Mrs. Gamp talk French? What is the French for *"veels within veels,"* and what verb means *"to be dispoged"*? Along with summers in France and the labours of editing and the diversion of private theatricals came the writing of a new novel on a large scale, *Little Dorrit*, begun in 1856 and published as a book in 1857. It is not one of his greatest books. It contains, for intimate readers of Dickens, the character of the tittering Flora, "fair, fat and forty," who is in a sense a return to earth of David Copperfield's sweet little Dora. It reflects the episode in Dickens's life when an adored, lost love of his youth, his real Dora—not seen for twenty years—reappeared in his life, as fat and tittering as all lost loves are. They ought to die and stay dead. So thought Dickens and took a mean revenge in fiction.

But the book is at least remarkable for the character of Edward Dorrit. This picture of the "prisoner of the Marshalsea" is one of the most notable things in Dickens's work. It is not only one of the most pathetic of his creations, but it is drawn with an artistic skill unsurpassed in any of his work. Nor is it done with Dickens's usual and wonted method of craftsmanship. Here he lays aside the romanticism that was the very soul of his earlier and his usual work and writes with the pen of a realist.

To understand the quoted extract one must recall a moment the salient features of the story. Here is Edward Dorrit, the prisoner of the Marshalsea. We see his first incarceration—restless, ashamed, and wistful for the freedom that he expects from hour to hour. It does not come. His wife dies in the prison leaving behind her a little child—little Dorrit. The years pass—ten, twenty —scarcely countable. Dorrit has grown old, shabby, inured to prison—with a sort of dusty dignity as the "Father of the Marshalsea." The turnkey "on the lock" treats him with a certain deference. He cadges for tips and gifts from strangers, almost lost to self-respect.

Then comes release in sudden wealth—great wealth. Dorrit flowers again, transformed into a munificent grandee but with something in his uncertain mind that still lies in the shadow of the prison wall. Thus rejuvenated he plans marriage with his daughter's chaperon, his enfeebled mind enlarges to new visions of grandeur —and then breaks in sudden final collapse. There is no grander thing in fiction than the climax of the scene below, when Mr. Dorrit asks if "Bob is on the lock." In the glitter and grandeur of his Italian palace the prison has closed again upon his fading senses.

Let the student of literature, who studies fiction in his college, note that Dorrit is drawn with the pen of a realist. The romanticist suffuses all his work with the colour of his own thought, interpreting everything, and exaggerating in order to interpret. Not so the realist. He shows a photographic copy of the things that are. He lets the facts speak for themselves. Either method may falter or fail. Romanticism can melt into slush; realism can dry out into a catalogue. Both are true and both may rise to eminence. Dickens's portraiture of Dorrit, as realistic art, could hardly be surpassed. Every word that Dorrit is made to say is exactly what Dorrit would have said.

MR. DORRIT ASKS IF BOB IS ON THE LOCK

THERE had been taken to the Marshalsea Prison, long before the day when the sun shone on Marseilles and on the opening of this narrative, a debtor with whom this narrative has some concern.

He was, at that time, a very amiable and very helpless middle-aged gentleman, who was going out again directly. Necessarily, he was going out again directly, because the Marshalsea lock never turned upon a debtor who was not. He brought in a portmanteau with him, which he doubted its being worth while to unpack; he was so perfectly clear—like all the rest of them, the turnkey on the lock said—that he was going out again directly.

He was a shy, retiring man; well-looking, though in an effeminate style; with a mild voice, curling hair, and irresolute hands—rings upon the fingers in those days—which nervously wandered to his trembling lip a hundred times in the first half-hour of his acquaintance with the jail. His principal anxiety was about his wife.

"Do you think, sir," he asked the turnkey, "that she will be very much shocked, if she should come to the gate tomorrow morning?"

The turnkey gave it as the result of his experience that some of 'em was and some of 'em wasn't. In general, more no than yes. "What like is she, you see?" he philosophically asked: "that's what it hinges on."

"She is very delicate and inexperienced indeed."

"That," said the turnkey, "is agen her."

"She is so little used to go out alone," said the debtor, "that I am at a loss to think how she will ever make her way here, if she walks."

"P'raps," quoth the turnkey, "she'll take a ackney coach."

"Perhaps." The irresolute fingers went to the trembling lip. "I hope she will. She may not think of it."

"Or p'raps," said the turnkey, offering his suggestions from the top of his well-worn wooden stool, as he might have offered them to a child for whose weakness he felt a compassion, "p'raps she'll get her brother, or her sister, to come along with her."

"She has no brother or sister."

"Niece, nevy, cousin, serwant, young 'ooman, greengrocer.—Dash it! One or another on 'em," said the turnkey, repudiating beforehand the refusal of all his suggestions.

"I fear—I hope it is not against the rules—that she will bring the children."

"The children?" said the turnkey. "And the rules? Why, lord set you up like a corner pin, we've a reg'lar playground o' children here. Children! Why we swarm with 'em. How many a you got?"

"Two," said the debtor, lifting his irresolute hand to his lip again, and turning into the prison.

The turnkey followed him with his eyes. "And you another," he observed to himself, "which makes three on you. And your wife another, I'll lay a crown. Which makes four on you. And another coming, I'll lay half-a-crown. Which'll make five on you. And I'll go another seven and sixpence to name which is the helplessest, the unborn baby or you!"

He was right in all his particulars. She came next day with a little boy of three years old, and a little girl of two, and he stood entirely corroborated.

"Got a room now; haven't you?" the turnkey asked the debtor after a week or two.

"Yes, I have got a very good room."

"Any little sticks a coming to furnish it?" said the turnkey.

"I expect a few necessary articles of furniture to be delivered by the carrier, this afternoon."

"Missis and little 'uns a coming to keep you company?" asked the turnkey.

"Why, yes, we think it better that we should not be scattered, even for a few weeks."

"Even for a few weeks, *of* course," replied the turnkey. And he followed him again with his eyes, and nodded his head seven times when he was gone.

*   *   *   *   *

Time went on, and the turnkey began to fail. His chest swelled, and his legs got weak, and he was short of breath. The well-worn wooden stool was "beyond him," he complained. He sat in an arm-chair with a

cushion, and sometimes wheezed so, for minutes together, that he couldn't turn the key. When he was overpowered by these fits, the debtor often turned it for him.

"You and me," said the turnkey, one snowy winter's
night when the lodge, with a bright fire in it, was pretty
full of company, "is the oldest inhabitants. I wasn't
here myself about seven year before you. I shan't last
long. When I'm off the lock for good and all, you'll be
the Father of the Marshalsea."

The turnkey went off the lock of this world next day.
His words were remembered and repeated; and tradi-
tion afterwards handed down from generation to generation—a Marshalsea generation might be calculated
as about three months—that the shabby old debtor
with the soft manner and the white hair, was the
Father of the Marshalsea.

And he grew to be proud of the title. If any impostor
had arisen to claim it, he would have shed tears in re-
sentment of the attempt to deprive him of his rights. A
disposition began to be perceived in him to exaggerate
the number of years he had been there; it was generally
understood that you must deduct a few from his account; he was vain, the fleeting generations of debtors
said.

All new-comers were presented to him. He was punc-
tilious in the exaction of this ceremony. The wits would
perform the office of introduction with overcharged
pomp and politeness, but they could not easily overstep

his sense of its gravity. He received them in his poor room (he disliked an introduction in the mere yard, as informal—a thing that might happen to anybody), with a kind of bowed-down beneficence. They were welcome to the Marshalsea, he would tell them. Yes, he was the Father of the place. So the world was kind enough to call him; and so he was, if more than twenty years of residence gave him a claim to the title. It looked small at first, but there was very good company there—among a mixture—necessarily a mixture—and very good air.

$$* \qquad * \qquad * \qquad * \qquad *$$

Little Dorrit, in her watchful love, would have remembered the lightest thing he said or did that night, though she had had no subsequent reason to recall that night. She always remembered that, when he looked about him under the strong influence of the old association, he tried to keep it out of her mind, and perhaps out of his own too, by immediately expatiating on the great riches and great company that had encompassed him in his absence, and on the lofty position he and his family had to sustain. Nor did she fail to recall that there were two under-currents, side by side, pervading all his discourse and all his manner; one showing her how well he had got on without her, and how independent he was of her; the other, in a fitful and unintelligible way almost complaining of her, as if it had been possible that she had neglected him while he was away.

His telling her of the glorious state that Mr. Merdle kept, and of the court that bowed before him, naturally brought him to Mrs. Merdle. So naturally indeed, that although there was an unusual want of sequence in the greater part of his remarks, he passed to her at once, and asked how she was.

"She is very well. She is going away next week."

"Home?" asked Mr. Dorrit.

"After a few weeks' stay upon the road."

"She will be a vast loss here," said Mr. Dorrit. "A vast—ha—acquisition at home. To Fanny, and to—hum—the rest of the—ha—great world."

Little Dorrit thought of the competition that was to be entered upon, and assented very softly.

"Mrs. Merdle is going to have a great farewell Assembly, dear, and a dinner before it. She has been expressing her anxiety that you should return in time. She has invited both you and me to her dinner."

"She is—ha—very kind. When is the day?"

"The day after to-morrow."

"Write round in the morning, and say that I have returned, and shall—hum—be delighted."

"May I walk with you up the stairs to your room, dear?"

"No!" he answered, looking angrily round; for he was moving away, as if forgetful of leave-taking. "You may not, Amy. I want no help. I am your father, not your infirm uncle!" He checked himself, as abruptly as he had broken into this reply, and said, "You have not kissed me, Amy. Good night, my dear! We must marry—ha—we must marry *you*, now." With that he went, more slowly and more tired, up the staircase to his rooms, and, almost as soon as he got there, dismissed his valet. His next care was to look about him for his Paris purchases, and, after opening their cases and carefully surveying them, to put them away under lock and key. After that, what with dozing and what with castle-building, he lost himself for a long time, so that there was a touch of morning on the eastward rim of the desolate Campagna when he crept to bed.

Mrs. General sent up her compliments in good time next day, and hoped he had rested well after this fatiguing journey. He sent down his compliments, and begged to inform Mrs. General that he had rested very well indeed, and was in high condition. Nevertheless, he did not come forth from his own rooms until late in the afternoon; and, although he then caused himself to be magnificently arrayed for a drive with Mrs. General and his daughter, his appearance was scarcely up to his description of himself.

As the family had no visitors that day, its four members dined alone together. He conducted Mrs. General to the seat at his right hand with immense ceremony; and Little Dorrit could not but notice as she followed with her uncle, both that he was again elaborately dressed, and that his manner towards Mrs. General was very particular. The perfect formation of that accomplished lady's surface rendered it difficult to displace an atom of its genteel glaze, but Little Dorrit thought she descried a slight thaw of triumph in a corner of her frosty eye.

Notwithstanding what may be called in these pages the Pruney and Prismatic nature of the family banquet, Mr. Dorrit several times fell asleep, while it was in progress. His fits of dozing were as sudden as they had been overnight, and were as short and profound. When the first of these slumberings seized him, Mrs. General looked almost amazed: but, on each recurrence of the symptoms, she told her polite beads, Papa, Potatoes, Poultry, Prunes, and Prism; and, by dint of going through that infallible performance very slowly, appeared to finish her rosary at about the same time as Mr. Dorrit started from his sleep.

He was again painfully aware of a somnolent tendency in Frederick (which had no existence out of his own imagination), and after dinner, when Frederick had withdrawn, privately apologised to Mrs. General for the poor man. "The most estimable and affectionate of brothers," he said, "but—ha, hum—broken up altogether. Unhappily, declining fast."

"Mr. Frederick, sir," quoth Mrs. General, "is habitually absent and drooping, but let us hope it is not so bad as that."

Mr. Dorrit, however, was determined not to let him off. "Fast declining, madam. A wreck. A ruin. Mouldering away before our eyes. Hum. Good Frederick!"

"You left Mrs. Sparkler quite well and happy, I

trust?" said Mrs. General, after heaving a cool sigh for Frederick.

"Surrounded," replied Mr. Dorrit, "by—ha—all that can charm the taste, and—hum—elevate the mind. Happy, my dear madam, in a—hum—husband."

Mrs. General was a little fluttered; seemingly delicately to put the word away with her gloves, as if there were no knowing what it might lead to.

"Fanny," Mr. Dorrit continued. "Fanny, Mrs. General, has high qualities. Ha. Ambition—hum—purpose, consciousness of—ha—position, determination to support that position—ha, hum—grace, beauty, and native nobility."

"No doubt," said Mrs. General (with a little extra stiffness).

"Combined with these qualities, madam," said Mr. Dorrit, "Fanny has—ha—manifested one blemish which has made me—hum—made me uneasy, and—ha —I must add, angry; but which I trust may now be considered at an end, even as to herself, and which is undoubtedly at an end as to—ha—others."

"To what, Mr. Dorrit," returned Mrs. General, with her gloves again somewhat excited, "can you allude? I am at a loss to——"

"Do not say that, my dear madam," interrupted Mr. Dorrit.

Mrs. General's voice, as it died away, pronounced the words, "at a loss to imagine."

After which Mr. Dorrit was seized with a doze for

about a minute, out of which he sprang with spasmodic nimbleness.

"I refer, Mrs. General, to that—ha—strong spirit of opposition, or—hum—I might say—ha—jealousy in Fanny, which has occasionally risen against the—ha—sense I entertain of—hum—the claims of—ha—the lady with whom I have now the honour of communing."

"Mr. Dorrit," returned Mrs. General, "is ever but too obliging, ever but too appreciative. If there have been moments when I have imagined that Miss Dorrit has indeed resented the favourable opinion Mr. Dorrit has formed of my services, I have found, in that only too high opinion, my consolation and recompense."

"Opinion of your services, madam?" said Mr. Dorrit.

"Of," Mrs. General repeated, in an elegantly impressive manner, "my services."

"Of your services alone, dear madam?" said Mr. Dorrit.

"I presume," retorted Mrs. General, in her former impressive manner, "of my services alone. For, to what else," said Mrs. General, with a slightly interrogative action of her gloves, "could I impute——"

"To—ha—yourself, Mrs. General. Ha, hum. To yourself and your merits," was Mr. Dorrit's rejoinder.

"Mr. Dorrit will pardon me," said Mrs. General, "if I remark that this is not a time or place for the pursuit of the present conversation. Mr. Dorrit will excuse me if I remind him that Miss Dorrit is in the adjoining room, and is visible to myself while I utter her name. Mr. Dorrit will forgive me if I observe that I am agitated, and that I find there are moments when weaknesses I supposed myself to have subdued, return with redoubled power. Mr. Dorrit will allow me to withdraw."

"Hum. Perhaps we may resume this—ha—interesting conversation," said Mr. Dorrit, "at another time; unless it should be, what I hope it is not—hum—in any way disagreeable to—ha—Mrs. General."

"Mr. Dorrit," said Mrs. General, casting down her eyes as she rose with a bend, "must ever claim my homage and obedience."

Mrs. General then took herself off in a stately way, and not with that amount of trepidation upon her which might have been expected in a less remarkable woman. Mr. Dorrit, who had conducted his part of the dialogue with a certain majestic and admiring condescension—much as some people may be seen to conduct themselves in Church, and to perform their part in the service—appeared, on the whole, very well satisfied with himself and with Mrs. General too. On the return of that lady to tea, she had touched herself up with a little powder and pomatum, and was not without moral enchantment likewise: the latter showing itself in much sweet patronage of manner towards Miss Dorrit, and in an air of as tender interest in Mr. Dorrit as was consistent with rigid propriety. At the close of the evening, when she rose to retire, Mr. Dorrit took her by the hand, as if he were going to lead her out into the Piazza of the people to walk a minuet by moonlight, and with great solemnity conducted her to the room door, where he raised her knuckles to his lips. Having parted from her with what may be conjectured to have been a rather bony kiss of a cosmetic flavour, he gave his daughter his blessing, graciously. And having thus hinted that there was something remarkable in the wind, he again went to bed.

He remained in the seclusion of his own chamber next morning; but, early in the afternoon, sent down his best compliments to Mrs. General, by Mr. Tinkler, and begged she would accompany Miss Dorrit on an airing without him. His daughter was dressed for Mrs. Merdle's dinner before he appeared. He then presented himself in a refulgent condition as to his attire, but looking indefinably shrunken and old. However, as he was plainly determined to be angry with her if she so much as asked him how he was, she only ventured to kiss his cheek, before accompanying him to Mrs. Merdle's with an anxious heart.

The distance that they had to go was very short, but he was at his building work again before the carriage had half traversed it. Mrs. Merdle received him with great distinction; the bosom was in admirable preservation, and on the best terms with itself; the dinner was very choice; and the company was very select.

It was principally English; saving that it comprised the usual French Count and the usual Italian Marchese

—decorative social milestones, always to be found in certain places, and varying very little in appearance. The table was long, and the dinner was long; and Little Dorrit, overshadowed by a large pair of black whiskers and a large white cravat, lost sight of her father altogether, until a servant put a scrap of paper in her hand, with a whispered request from Mrs. Merdle that she would read it directly. Mrs. Merdle had written on it in pencil, "Pray come and speak to Mr. Dorrit, I doubt if he is well."

She was hurrying to him, unobserved, when he got up out of his chair, and leaning over the table called to her, supposing her to be still in her place:

"Amy, Amy, my child!"

The action was so unusual, to say nothing of his strange eager appearance and strange eager voice, that it instantaneously caused a profound silence.

"Amy, my dear," he repeated. "Will you go and see if Bob is on the lock?"

She was at his side, and touching him, but he still perversely supposed her to be in her seat, and called out, still leaning over the table, "Amy, Amy. I don't feel quite myself. Ha. I don't know what's the matter with me. I particularly wish to see Bob. Ha. Of all the turnkeys, he's as much my friend as yours. See if Bob is in the lodge, and beg him to come to me."

All the guests were now in consternation, and everybody rose.

"Dear father, I am not there; I am here, by you."

"Oh! You are here, Amy! Good. Hum. Good. Ha. Call Bob. If he has been relieved, and is not on the lock, tell Mrs. Bangham to go and fetch him."

She was gently trying to get him away; but he resisted, and would not go.

"I tell you, child," he said petulantly, "I can't be got up the narrow stairs without Bob. Ha. Send for Bob. Hum. Send for Bob—best of all the turnkeys—send for Bob!"

He looked confusedly about him, and, becoming conscious of the number of faces by which he was surrounded, addressed them:

"Ladies and gentlemen, the duty—ha—devolves upon me of—hum—welcoming you to the Marshalsea! Welcome to the Marshalsea! The space is—ha—limited —limited—the parade might be wider; but you will find it apparently grow larger after a time—a time, ladies and gentlemen—and the air is, all things considered, very good. It blows over the ha—Surrey— hills. Blows over the Surrey hills. This is the Snuggery. Hum. Supported by a small subscription of the—ha— Collegiate body. In return for which—hot water—general kitchen—and little domestic advantages. Those who are habituated to the—ha—Marshalsea, are pleased to call me its Father. I am accustomed to be complimented by strangers as the—ha—Father of the Marshalsea. Certainly, if years of residence may establish a claim to so—ha—honourable a title, I may accept the

—hum—conferred distinction. My child, ladies and gentlemen. My daughter. Born here!"

She was not ashamed of it, or ashamed of him. She was pale and frightened; but she had no other care than to soothe him and get him away, for his own dear sake. She was between him and the wondering faces, turned round upon his breast with her own face raised to his. He held her clasped in his left arm, and between whiles her low voice was heard tenderly imploring him to go away with her.

"Born here," he repeated, shedding tears. "Bred here. Ladies and gentlemen, my daughter. Child of an unfortunate father, but—ha—always a gentleman. Poor, no doubt, but—hum—proud. Always proud. It has become a—hum—not infrequent custom for my—ha—personal admirers—personal admirers solely to—be pleased to express their desire to acknowledge my semi-official position here, by offering—ha—little tributes, which usually take the form of—ha—Testimonials—pecuniary Testimonials. In the acceptance of those—ha—voluntary recognitions of my humble endeavours to—hum—to uphold a Tone here—a Tone —I beg it to be understood that I do not consider myself compromised. Ha. Not compromised. Ha. Not a beggar. No; I repudiate the title! At the same time far be it from me to—hum—to put upon the fine feelings by which my partial friends are actuated, the slight of scrupling to admit that those offerings are—hum—highly acceptable. On the contrary, they are most ac-

ceptable. In my child's name, if not in my own, I
make the admission in the fullest manner, at the same
time reserving—ha—shall I say my personal dignity?
Ladies and gentlemen, God bless you all!"

By this time, the exceeding mortification undergone
by the Bosom had occasioned the withdrawal of the
greater part of the company into other rooms. The few
who had lingered thus long followed the rest, and Little
Dorrit and her father were left to the servants and
themselves. Dearest and most precious to her, he would
come with her now, would he not? He replied to her
fervid entreaties, that he would never be able to get
up the narrow stairs without Bob; where was Bob,
would nobody fetch Bob? Under pretence of looking
for Bob, she got him out against the stream of gay
company now pouring in for the evening assembly, and
got him into a coach that had just set down its load,
and got him home.

The broad stairs of his Roman palace were contracted
in his failing sight to the narrow stairs of his London
prison; and he would suffer no one but her to touch him,
his brother excepted. They got him up to his room
without help, and laid him down on his bed. And from
that hour his poor maimed spirit, only remembering
the place where it had broken its wings, cancelled the
dream through which it had since groped, and knew of
nothing beyond the Marshalsea. When he heard footsteps in the street, he took them for the old weary tread
in the yards. When the hour came for locking up, he

supposed all strangers to be excluded for the night. When the time for opening came again, he was so anxious to see Bob, that they were fain to patch up a narrative how that Bob—many a year dead then, gentle turnkey—had taken cold, but hoped to be out to-morrow, or the next day, or the next at furthest.

He fell away into a weakness so extreme that he could not raise his hand. But he still protected his brother according to his long usage; and would say with some complacency, fifty times a day, when he saw him standing by his bed, "My good Frederick, sit down. You are very feeble indeed."

They tried him with Mrs. General, but he had not the faintest knowledge of her. Some injurious suspicion lodged itself in his brain, that she wanted to supplant Mrs. Bangham, and that she was given to drinking. He charged her with it in no measured terms; and was so urgent with his daughter to go round to the Marshal and entreat him to turn her out, that she was never re-produced after the first failure.

Saving that he once asked "if Tip had gone outside?" the remembrance of his two children not present seemed to have departed from him. But the child who had done so much for him and had been so poorly repaid, was never out of his mind. Not that he spared her, or was fearful of her being spent by watching and fatigue; he was not more troubled on that score than he had usually been. No; he loved her in his old way. They were in the jail again, and she tended him, and he had constant

need of her, and could not turn without her; and he even
told her, sometimes, that he was content to have undergone a great deal for her sake. As to her, she bent over
his bed with her quiet face against his, and would have
laid down her own life to restore him.

When he had been sinking in this painless way for two
or three days, she observed him to be troubled by
the ticking of his watch—a pompous gold watch that
made as great a to-do about its going as if nothing else
went but itself and Time. She suffered it to run down;
but he was still uneasy, and showed that was not what
he wanted. At length he roused himself to explain that
he wanted money to be raised on this watch. He was
quite pleased when she pretended to take it away for the
purpose, and afterwards had a relish for his little tastes
of wine and jelly, that he had not had before.

He soon made it plain that this was so; for, in another
day or two he sent off his sleeve-buttons and finger-
rings. He had an amazing satisfaction to entrusting
her with these errands, and appeared to consider it
equivalent to making the most methodical and provi-
dent arrangements. After his trinkets, or such of them
as he had been able to see about him, were gone, his
clothes engaged his attention; and it is as likely as not
that he was kept alive for some days by the satisfaction
of sending them, piece by piece, to an imaginary pawn-
broker's.

Thus for ten days Little Dorrit bent over his pillow,
laying her cheek against his. Sometimes she was so worn

out that for a few minutes they would slumber together. Then she would awake; to recollect with fast-flowing silent tears what it was that touched her face, and to see, stealing over the cherished face upon the pillow, a deeper shadow than the shadow of the Marshalsea Wall.

Quietly, quietly, all the lines of the plan of the great Castle melted, one after another. Quietly, quietly, the ruled and cross-ruled countenance on which they were traced, became fair and blank. Quietly, quietly, the reflected marks of the prison bars and of the zig-zag iron on the wall-top, faded away. Quietly, quietly, the face subsided into a far younger likeness of her own than she had ever seen under the gray hair, and sank to rest.

THE ASHES BURN OUT ON THE HEARTH
1858–1868

Chapter Nine

THE ASHES BURN OUT ON THE HEARTH

1858–1868

WITH the year 1858, in the month of May, came the unhappy break in Dickens's domestic life. He separated from his wife, or perhaps one might more properly say, he put his wife aside. Intimate friends of the family had long known that the marriage had not proved congenial. "Poor Catherine and I are not made for each other," so Dickens had written to John Foster, his closest friend, some time before, "and there is no help for it." The separation once made, Dickens, with extraordinary arrogance, expected all his friends and his readers to keep silent about it and to treat it as a trivial matter. He drew up a statement to the effect that he and his wife had agreed to part and printed it in *Household Words*. He even insisted that Bradbury & Evans, the proprietors, should print it also in their other journal, *Punch*. They drew the line at distressing that youthful and cheerful creature with the sorrows of matrimonial failure. Dickens broke off all relations with them as publishers, bought up the magazine and substituted a new one, *All the Year Round*. With this he expected, like a schoolmaster, to "hear no more about it." His friends maintained a loyal conspiracy of silence, still unbroken; but careless and evil tongues whispered. It is probable that Dickens had become an almost impossible husband: the strain of constant overwork, the preoccupation of creative art, the egotism of genius made him imperious and intolerant. He fretted over trifles. He brooked no criticism. Any fool could cut him to the heart. Yet we do not hear that his wife wanted the break. She left his home. The children stayed. The eldest son, now of age, went with her but married within a year or two. It seems a cruel fate for a woman who had borne ten children—quite a Dickens plot.

Yet after that Charles Dickens, it would seem, knew but little peace. The children, too, were leaving home for school, the army and the navy and the world. Presently only his daughter Mary remained. His sister-in-law, Georgina Hogarth, lived with him and kept his house and was with him when he died. His wife he never saw again. In his will he heaps money and praise upon his sister-in-law; for his wife, a small annuity without a parting word.

But from this time on Dickens lived in a fret and fever of overwork and overstrain. Even with the beautiful country home at his disposal, which he had bought at Gad's Hill, in Kent, he flitted restlessly from place to place seeking repose and finding it nowhere. The years closed in, relentless, upon him.

CHARLES DICKENS, HIS WIFE and SISTER
(Drawn by Maclise in 1842)

It was this situation, in part at least, that induced him to take up the public lecturing that ultimately hastened his end. He had, intermittently for years, given "readings" from his works, a practice originating from the night when he read *The Chimes* to his friends (1849). But these were random performances for this or that charity. But Dickens now (1858) began those great series of reading tours which electrified the British public, and later took America by storm. It is hard to find a single word to indicate what Charles Dickens did on the platform. It was not exactly "reading," nor "lecturing," nor "acting." It was a sort of mesmeric rendition of his works—with voice and words and gesture to aid in the illusion. Of the effect there is no doubt: the public were carried away in gales of laughter over the exploits of Mr. Pickwick, and were melted into tears at the deathbed of little Paul Dombey, or hushed and horror-stricken in the presence of the murderer Bill Sikes. Often it happened that women were carried from the hall in a faint; and that people sat motionless, gazing as if hypnotized into terror. . . .

But with it went an inconceivably great strain. Dickens never spared himself. He rehearsed for hours every word, every gesture; he lost himself in the intense concentration of his work, and after it, fell, shattered and exhausted. . . .

With this heavy strain there went the constant labour, in person or in voluminous correspondence, of his editorial work. And there was added further his continued writing. One great book at least dates from these closing years—the *Tale of Two Cities*. Few people will claim that it has the humour of the earlier books. But there is a majesty and a grandeur about Dickens's epic conception of the French Revolution that sustains the book. Nor must one think of it, as so many people do, as a historical novel. To Dickens in his youth, the French Revolution was a thing of yesterday, easily remembered by the older people round him. He himself was born three years and four months before the battle of Waterloo. The dim memories of his childhood may easily be included in the vision of the stagecoaches that started out from London in the glory of a June morning, gay with green branches and flags, shouting the news of the great victory. Apart from recollections and hearsay and his own visions of France, Dickens took much—of his theory of the Revolution at least—from Carlyle's famous work, one of his bedside books. This is no longer the comic France of his Pen Pictures and sketches. Yet there is in it a sort of element of the stage, making his Revolution, in a sense, a vast panorama of actors. And like the stage, it lends itself to climax. There is nothing better known in all of Dickens's books than the fate of Sydney Carton—the ne'er-do-well, in love with another man's wife, who takes the other man's place in the prison of the condemned—drugs him to get his place—and then dies in his stead on the guillotine.

SYDNEY CARTON GOES TO THE GUILLOTINE

IN THE BLACK PRISON of the Conciergerie, the doomed of the day awaited their fate. They were in number as the weeks of the year. Fifty-two were to roll that afternoon on the life-tide of the city to the boundless everlasting sea. Before their cells were quit of them, new occupants were appointed; before their blood ran into the blood spilled yesterday, the blood that was to mingle with theirs to-morrow was already set apart.

Two score and twelve were told off. From the farmer-general of seventy, whose riches could not buy his life, to the seamstress of twenty, whose poverty and obscurity could not save her. Physical diseases, engendered in the vices and neglects of men, will seize on victims of all degrees; and the frightful moral disorder, born of unspeakable suffering, intolerable oppression, and heartless indifference, smote equally without distinction.

Charles Darnay, alone in a cell, had sustained himself with no flattering delusion since he came to it from the Tribunal. In every line of the narrative he had heard, he had heard his condemnation. He had fully comprehended that no personal influence could possibly save him, that he was virtually sentenced by the millions, and that units could avail him nothing.

Nevertheless, it was not easy, with the face of his beloved wife fresh before him, to compose his mind to what it must bear. His hold on life was strong, and it was very, very hard, to loosen; by gradual efforts and degrees unclosed a little here, it clenched the tighter there; and when he brought his strength to bear on that hand and it yielded, this was closed again. There was a hurry, too, in all his thoughts, a turbulent and heated working of his heart, that contended against resignation. If, for a moment, he did feel resigned, then his wife and child who had to live after him, seemed to protest and to make it a selfish thing.

But, all this was at first. Before long, the consideration that there was no disgrace in the fate he must meet, and that numbers went the same road wrongfully, and trod it firmly every day, sprang up to stimulate him. Next followed the thought that much of the future peace of mind enjoyable by the dear ones, depended on his quiet fortitude. So, by degrees he calmed into the better state, when he could raise his thoughts much higher, and draw comfort down.

Before it had set in dark on the night of his condemnation, he had travelled thus far on his last way. Being allowed to purchase the means of writing, and a light, he sat down to write until such time as the prison lamps should be extinguished.

He wrote a long letter to Lucie, showing her that he had known nothing of her father's imprisonment, until he had heard of it from herself, and that he had been as ignorant as she of his father's and uncle's responsibility for that misery, until the paper had been read.

He had already explained to her that his concealment
from herself of the name he had relinquished, as the
one condition—fully intelligible now—that her father
had attached to their betrothal, and was the one promise
he had still exacted on the morning of their marriage.
He entreated her, for her father's sake, never to seek
to know whether her father had become oblivious of
the existence of the paper, or had had it recalled to
him (for the moment, or for good) by the story of the
Tower, on that old Sunday under the dear old plane-tree
in the garden. If he had preserved any definite remembrance of it, there could be no doubt that he had supposed it destroyed with the Bastille, when he had found
no mention of it among the relics of prisoners which the
populace had discovered there, and which had been described to all the world. He besought her—though he
added that he knew it was needless—to console her
father, by impressing him through every tender means
she could think of, with the truth that he had done nothing for which he could justly reproach himself, but had
uniformly forgotten himself for their joint sakes. Next
to her preservation of his own last grateful love and
blessing, and her overcoming of her sorrow, to devote
herself to their dear child, he adjured her, as they
would meet in Heaven, to comfort her father.

To her father himself, he wrote in the same strain;
but, he told her father that he expressly confided his
wife and child to his care. And he told him this, very
strongly, with the hope of rousing him from any de-

spondency or dangerous retrospect towards which he foresaw he might be tending.

To Mr. Lorry, he commended them all, and explained his worldly affairs. That done, with many added sentences of grateful friendship and warm attachment, all was done. He never thought of Carton. His mind was so full of the others, that he never once thought of him.

He had time to finish these letters before the lights were put out. When he lay down on his straw bed, he thought he had done with this world.

But, it beckoned him back in his sleep, and showed itself in shining forms. Free and happy, back in the old house in Soho (though it had nothing in it like the real house), unaccountably released and light of heart, he was with Lucie again, and she told him it was all a dream, and he had never gone away. A pause of forgetfulness, and then he had even suffered, and had come back to her, dead and at peace, and yet there was no difference in him. Another pause of oblivion, and he awoke in the sombre morning, unconscious where he was or what had happened, until it flashed upon his mind, "this is the day of my death!"

Thus, had he come through the hours, to the day when the fifty-two heads were to fall. And now, while he was composed, and hoped that he could meet the end with quiet heroism, a new action began in his waking thoughts, which was very difficult to master.

He had never seen the instrument that was to ter-

minate his life. How high it was from the ground, how
many steps it had, where he would be stood, how he
would be touched, whether the touching hands would
be dyed red, which way his face would be turned,
whether he would be the first, or might be the last:
these and many similar questions, in no wise directed
by his will, obtruded themselves over and over again,
countless times. Neither were they connected with fear:
he was conscious of no fear. Rather, they originated in a
strange besetting desire to know what to do when the
time came; a desire gigantically disproportionate to the
few swift moments to which it referred; a wondering
what was more like the wondering of some other spirit
within his, than his own.

The hours went on as he walked to and fro, and the
clocks struck the numbers he would never hear again.
Nine gone for ever, ten gone for ever, eleven gone for
ever, twelve coming on to pass away. After a hard con-
test with that eccentric action of thought which had
last perplexed him, he had got the better of it. He
walked up and down, softly repeating their names to
himself. The worst of the strife was over. He could
walk up and down, free from distracting fancies, pray-
ing for himself and for them.

Twelve gone for ever.

He had been apprised that the final hour was Three,
and he knew he would be summoned some time earlier,
inasmuch as the tumbrils jolted heavily and slowly

through the streets. Therefore, he resolved to keep Two before his mind, as the hour, and so to strengthen himself in the interval that he might be able, after that time, to strengthen others.

Walking regularly to and fro with his arms folded on his breast, a very different man from the prisoner who had walked to and fro at La Force, he heard One struck away from him, without surprise. The hour had measured like most other hours. Devoutly thankful to Heaven for his recovered self-possession, he thought, "There is but another now," and turned to walk again.

Footsteps in the stone passage outside the door. He stopped.

The key was put in the lock, and turned. Before the door was opened, or as it opened, a man said in a low voice, in English: "He has never seen me here; I have kept out of his way. Go you in alone; I wait near. Lose no time!"

The door was quickly opened and closed, and there stood before him face to face, quiet, intent upon him, with the light of a smile on his features, and a cautionary finger on his lip, Sydney Carton.

There was something so bright and remarkable in his look, that, for the first moment, the prisoner misdoubted him to be an apparition of his own imagining. But, he spoke, and it was his voice; he took the prisoner's hand, and it was his real grasp.

"Of all the people upon earth, you least expected to see me?" he said.

"I could not believe it to be you. I can scarcely believe it now. You are not"—the apprehension came suddenly into his mind—"a prisoner?"

"No. I am accidentally possessed of a power over one
of the keepers here, and in virtue of it I stand before you.
I come from her—your wife, dear Darnay."

The prisoner wrung his hand.

"I bring you a request from her."

"What is it?"

"A most earnest, pressing, and emphatic entreaty, addressed to you in the most pathetic tones of the voice so
dear to you, that you well remember."

The prisoner turned his face partly aside.

"You have no time to ask me why I bring it, or what
it means; I have no time to tell you. You must comply
with it—take off those boots you wear, and draw on
these of mine."

There was a chair against the wall of the cell, behind
the prisoner. Carton, pressing forward, had already,
with the speed of lightning, got him down into it, and
stood over him, barefoot.

"Draw on these boots of mine. Put your hands to
them; put your will to them. Quick!"

"Carton, there is no escaping from this place; it never
can be done. You will only die with me. It is madness."

"It would be madness if I asked you to escape; but
do I? When I ask you to pass out at that door, tell me it
is madness and remain here. Change that cravat for
this of mine, that coat for this of mine. While you do it,

let me take this ribbon from your hair, and shake out your hair like this of mine!"

With wonderful quickness, and with a strength both of will and action, that appeared quite supernatural, he forced all these changes upon him. The prisoner was like a young child in his hands.

"Carton! Dear Carton! It is madness. It cannot be accomplished, it never can be done, it has been attempted, and has always failed. I implore you not to add your death to the bitterness of mine."

"Do I ask you, my dear Darnay, to pass the door? When I ask that, refuse. There are pen and ink and paper on this table. Is your hand steady enough to write?"

"It was when you came in."

"Steady it again, and write what I shall dictate. Quick, friend, quick!"

Pressing his hand to his bewildered head, Darnay sat down at the table. Carton, with his right hand in his breast, stood close beside him.

"Write exactly as I speak."

"To whom do I address it?"

"To no one." Carton still had his hand in his breast.

"Do I date it?"

"No."

The prisoner looked up, at each question. Carton, standing over him with his hand in his breast, looked down.

"'If you remember,'" said Carton, dictating, "'the

words that passed between us, long ago, you will readily comprehend this when you see it. You do remember them, I know. It is not in your nature to forget them."

He was drawing his hand from his breast; the prisoner chancing to look up in his hurried wonder as he wrote, the hand stopped, closing upon something.

"Have you written 'forget them'?" Carton asked.

"I have. Is that a weapon in your hand?"

"No; I am not armed."

"What is it in your hand?"

"You shall know directly. Write on; there are but a few words more." He dictated again. "'I am thankful that the time has come, when I can prove them. That I do so is no subject for regret or grief.'" As he said these words with his eyes fixed on the writer, his hand slowly and softly moved down close to the writer's face.

The pen dropped from Darnay's fingers on the table, and he looked about him vacantly.

"What vapour is that?" he asked.

"Vapour?"

"Something that crossed me?"

"I am conscious of nothing; there can be nothing here. Take up the pen and finish. Hurry, hurry!"

As if his memory were impaired or his faculties disordered, the prisoner made an effort to rally his attention. As he looked at Carton with clouded eyes and with an altered manner of breathing, Carton—his hand again in his breast—looked steadily at him.

"Hurry, hurry!"

The prisoner bent over the paper, once more.

"'If it had been otherwise;'" Carton's hand was again watchfully and softly stealing down; "'I never should have used the longer opportunity. If it had been otherwise;'" the hand was at the prisoner's face; "'I should but have had so much the more to answer for. If it had been otherwise——'" Carton looked at the pen and saw it was trailing off into unintelligible signs.

Carton's hand moved back to his breast no more. The prisoner sprang up with a reproachful look, but Carton's hand was close and firm at his nostrils, and Carton's left arm caught him round the waist. For a few seconds he faintly struggled with the man who had come to lay down his life for him; but, within a minute or so, he was stretched insensible on the ground.

Quickly, but with hands as true to the purpose as his heart was, Carton dressed himself in the clothes the prisoner had laid aside, combed back his hair, and tied it with the ribbon the prisoner had worn. Then, he softly called, "Enter there! Come in!" and the Spy presented himself.

"You see?" said Carton, looking up, as he kneeled on one knee beside the insensible figure, putting the paper in the breast: "is your hazard very great?"

"Mr. Carton," the Spy answered, with a timid snap of his fingers, "my hazard is not *that*, in the thick of business here, if you are true to the whole of your bargain."

"Don't fear me. I will be true to the death."

"You must be, Mr. Carton, if the tale of fifty-two is to be right. Being made right by you in that dress, I shall have no fear."

"Have no fear! I shall soon be out of the way of harming you, and the rest will soon be far from here, please God! Now, get assistance and take me to the coach."

"You?" said the Spy, nervously.

"Him, man, with whom I have exchanged. You go out at the gate by which you brought me in?"

"Of course."

"I was weak and faint when you brought me in, and I am fainter now you take me out. The parting interview has overpowered me. Such a thing has happened here, often, and too often. Your life is in your own hands. Quick! Call assistance!"

"You swear not to betray me?" said the trembling Spy, as he paused for a last moment.

"Man, man!" returned Carton, stamping his foot; "have I sworn by no solemn vow already, to go through with this, that you waste the precious moments now? Take him yourself to the court-yard you know of, place him yourself in the carriage, show him yourself to Mr. Lorry, tell him yourself to give him no restorative but air, and to remember my words of last night, and his promise of last night, and drive away!"

The Spy withdrew, and Carton seated himself at the table, resting his forehead on his hands. The Spy returned immediately with two men.

"How then?" said one of them, contemplating the fallen figure. "So afflicted to find that his friend has drawn a prize in the lottery of Sainte Guillotine?"

"A good patriot," said the other, "could hardly have been more afflicted if the Aristocrat had drawn a blank."

They raised the unconscious figure, placed it on a litter they had brought to the door, and bent to carry it away.

"The time is short, Evrémonde," said the Spy, in a warning voice.

"I know it well," answered Carton. "Be careful of my friend, I entreat you, and leave me."

"Come, then, my children," said Barsad. "Lift him, and come away!"

The door closed, and Carton was left alone. Straining his powers of listening to the utmost, he listened for any sound that might denote suspicion or alarm. There was none. Keys turned, doors clashed, footsteps passed along distant passages: no cry was raised, or hurry made, that seemed unusual. Breathing more freely in a little while, he sat down at the table, and listened again until the clock struck Two.

Sounds that he was not afraid of, for he divined their meaning, then began to be audible. Several doors were opened in succession, and finally his own. A jailer, with a list in his hand, looked in, merely saying, "Follow me, Evrémonde!" and he followed into a large dark room, at a distance. It was a dark winter day, and what with the shadows within, and what with the shadows without, he could but dimly discern the others who were brought there to have their arms bound. Some were standing; some seated. Some were lamenting, and in restless motion; but these were few. The great majority were silent and still, looking fixedly at the ground.

As he stood by the wall in a dim corner, while some of the fifty-two were brought in after him, one man stopped in passing, to embrace him, as having a knowledge of him. It thrilled him with a great dread of discovery; but the man went on. A very few moments after that, a young woman, with a slight girlish form, a sweet spare face in which there was no vestige of colour, and large widely opened patient eyes, rose from the seat where he had observed her sitting, and came to speak to him.

"Citizen Evrémonde," she said, touching him with her cold hand. "I am a poor little seamstress, who was with you in La Force."

He murmured for answer: "True. I forget what you were accused of?"

"Plots. Though the just Heaven knows I am innocent of any. Is it likely? Who would think of plotting with a poor little weak creature like me?"

The forlorn smile with which she said it, so touched him, that tears started from his eyes.

"I am not afraid to die, Citizen Evrémonde, but I

have done nothing. I am not unwilling to die, if the Republic which is to do so much good to us poor, will profit by my death; but I do not know how that can be, Citizen Evrémonde. Such a poor weak little creature!"

As the last thing on earth that his heart was to warm and soften to, it warmed and softened to this pitiable girl.

"I heard you were released, Citizen Evrémonde. I hoped it was true?"

"It was. But, I was again taken and condemned."

"If I may ride with you, Citizen Evrémonde, will you let me hold your hand? I am not afraid, but I am little and weak, and it will give me more courage."

As the patient eyes were lifted to his face, he saw a sudden doubt in them, and then astonishment. He pressed the work-worn, hunger-worn young fingers, and touched his lips.

"Are you dying for him?" she whispered.

"And his wife and child. Hush! Yes."

"Oh you will let me hold your brave hand, stranger?"

"Hush! Yes, my poor sister; to the last."

The same shadows that are falling on the prison, are falling, in that same hour of the early afternoon, on the Barrier with the crowd about it, when a coach going out of Paris drives up to be examined.

"Who goes here? Whom have we within? Papers!"

The papers were handed out, and read.

"Alexandre Manette. Physician. French. Which is he?"

This is he; this helpless, inarticulately murmuring, wandering old man pointed out.

"Apparently the Citizen-Doctor is not in his right mind? The Revolution-fever will have been too much for him?"

Greatly too much for him.

"Hah! Many suffer with it. Lucie. His daughter. French. Which is she?"

This is she.

"Apparently it must be. Lucie, the wife of Evrémonde; is it not?"

It is.

"Hah! Evrémonde has an assignation elsewhere. Lucie, her child. English. This is she?"

She and no other.

"Kiss me, child of Evrémonde. Now, thou hast kissed a good Republican; something new in thy family; remember it! Sydney Carton. Advocate. English. Which is he?"

He lies here, in this corner of the carriage. He, too, is pointed out.

"Apparently the English advocate is in a swoon?"

It is hoped he will recover in the fresher air. It is represented that he is not in strong health, and has separated sadly from a friend who is under the displeasure of the Republic.

"Is that all? It is not a great deal, that! Many are

under the displeasure of the Republic, and must look out at the little window. Jarvis Lorry. Banker. English. Which is he?"

"I am he. Necessarily, being the last."

It is Jarvis Lorry who has replied to all the previous questions. It is Jarvis Lorry who has alighted and stands with his hand on the coach door, replying to a group of officials. They leisurely walk round the carriage and leisurely mount the box, to look at what little luggage it carries on the roof; the country-people hanging about, press nearer to the coach doors and greedily stare in; a little child, carried by its mother, has its short arm held out for it, that it may touch the wife of an aristocrat who has gone to the Guillotine.

"Behold your papers, Jarvis Lorry, countersigned."

"One can depart, citizen?"

"One can depart. Forward, my postilions! A good journey!"

"I salute you, citizens.—And the first danger passed!"

These are again the words of Jarvis Lorry, as he clasps his hands, and looks upward. There is terror in the carriage, there is weeping, there is the heavy breathing of the insensible traveller.

"Are we not going too slowly? Can they not be induced to go faster?" asks Lucie, clinging to the old man.

"It would seem like flight, my darling. I must not urge them too much; it would rouse suspicion."

"Look back, look back, and see if we are pursued!"

"The road is clear, my dearest. So far, we are not pursued."

Houses in twos and threes pass by us, solitary farms, ruinous buildings, dye-works, tanneries, and the like, open country avenues, of leafless trees. The hard uneven pavement is under us, the soft deep mud is on either side. Sometimes, we strike into the skirting mud, to avoid the stones that clatter us and shake us; sometimes we stick in ruts and sloughs there. The agony of our impatience is then so great, that in our wild alarm and hurry we are for getting out and running—hiding— doing anything but stopping.

Out of the open country, in again among ruinous buildings, solitary farms, dye-works, tanneries, and the like, cottages in twos and threes, avenues of leafless trees. Have these men deceived us, and taken us back by another road? Is not this the same place twice over? Thank Heaven, no. A village. Look back, look back, and see if we are pursued! Hush! the posting-house.

Leisurely, our four horses are taken out; leisurely, the coach stands in the little street, bereft of horses, and with no likelihood upon it of ever moving again; leisurely, the new horses come into visible existence, one by one; leisurely, the new postilions follow, sucking and plaiting the lashes of their whips; leisurely, the old postilions count their money, make wrong additions, and arrive at dissatisfied results. All the time, our overfraught hearts are beating at a rate that would far outstrip the fastest gallop of the fastest horses ever foaled.

At length the new postilions are in their saddles, and the old are left behind. We are through the village, up the hill, and down the hill, and on the low watery grounds. Suddenly, the postilions exchange speech with animated gesticulation, and the horses are pulled up, almost on their haunches. We are pursued?

"Ho! Within the carriage there. Speak, then!"

"What is it?" asks Mr. Lorry, looking out at window.

"How many did they say?"

"I do not understand you."

"—At the last post. How many to the Guillotine to-day?"

"Fifty-two."

"I said so! A brave number! My fellow-citizen here would have it forty-two; ten more heads are worth having. The Guillotine goes handsomely. I love it. Hi forward. Whoop!"

The night comes on dark. He moves more; he is beginning to revive, and to speak intelligibly; he thinks they are still together; he asks him by his name, what he has in his hand. O pity us, kind Heaven, and help us! Look out, look out, and see if we are pursued.

The wind is rushing after us, and the clouds are flying after us, and the moon is plunging after us, and the whole wild night is in pursuit of us; but, so far, we are pursued by nothing else.

AND AFTER THAT THE DARK
1868–1870

Chapter Ten

AND AFTER THAT THE DARK
1868–1870

Dickens had followed up the success of his *Tale of Two Cities* with a number of smaller stories in his journal *All the Year Round*, and with two full-length novels, *Great Expectations* (1861) and *Our Mutual Friend* (1865). Dickens's books to Dickens's lovers are as whiskey is said to be to the colonels of Kentucky—no such thing as bad ones. But most people admit that *Great Expectations*, in spite of its fine opening, does not fulfil its own title; and many people class *Our Mutual Friend* as a poor book, the product of an exhausted mind and a jaded imagination. Dickens was harassed by the strain of his lecture work and by the increasing emptiness of his home; an experience in a terrible railway accident (June 9, 1865) had shaken him in body and mind. He was no longer suited to the exigencies of writing in instalments for fixed dates.

Yet in spite of increasing fatigue and growing danger he could not resist the financial temptation of a proposed tour in America. Dickens's lecture tour in the

United States lasted from December, 1867, to April, 1868. He spoke only in the greater cities of the East. There was no need to seek for audiences. The crowds fought for tickets: in Brooklyn they lay out all night on mattresses waiting for a chance to buy.

But Dickens was no longer the ardent and untiring visitor of 1842. He was utterly broken and exhausted and must lie inert for hours to gather strength. Nor had he any interest in his tour beyond the art of his own performance and a feverish interest in the tremendous returns of the box office. (Gross receipts $228,000 paper: Dickens's share £19,000 gold.) But America itself he never saw and for it cared nothing. Yet this was just after the close of the Civil War. Nearly all the great figures of the epic struggle, except the greatest, were still upon the scene. Dickens never bothered with them. Once he met Stanton, Lincoln's Secretary of War, with whom he spent his time capping quotations from his own books. Yet even to his harassed and breaking mind there came some consciousness of the wonderful receptions, the universal kindness that he met, and the generous forgiveness of his former misdeeds. As some measure of return he broke his fixed rule and attended just at the end (April 18, 1868) a public dinner in his honour at Delmonico's in New York. There he spoke the words of his *amende honorable* to America, which are printed in all editions of his "American" books.

Dickens arrived in England in May of 1868, much recuperated by the voyage. He resumed his editorial work, and soon embarked on the last of his series of public readings (1868-1869). For these he rehearsed new pieces, above all a murder scene of appalling horror reconstructed out of the crime of Sikes of *Oliver Twist*. The lectures were a terrific success, the halls crowded to suffocation; the audience swept away in an ecstasy of feeling. Witness the words of Macready, Dickens's old actor friend, or rather Macready's lack of words to convey his appreciation. Macready was speaking of an earlier tour (Cheltenham, 1862), but the later performances were if anything of greater power. But the price that Dickens was to pay for his success was his own life. The compiler of the present volume in a larger work* has thus described his condition: "He was exhausted. He was sleepless. He lay for hours upon sofas waiting for strength. His sight failed. At times on the street he could see only half of the letters on the shops—the top, not the bottom. Words slipped from him. Gaps opened in his memory. His hands groped wrongly in the air for things elsewhere. If he wished to lay his left hand on the table he must look first where it was to go. At times he could not raise his hand up to his head. His left foot was a dead weight. This was paralysis—cerebral hæmorrhage—approaching—imminent. As Dickens stood upon the lecture platform there was a shrouded figure standing behind him waiting to strike."

Charles Dickens: His Life and Work, by Stephen Leacock, Doubleday, Doran, 1933.

The firm insistence of a great physician dragged Dickens from the platform and for the time being saved his life. A little later, reappearing for a few final readings in London, he said farewell forever to his public audiences, closing his last reading of *Pickwick* with the memorable words, "From the garish lights I vanish now forevermore, with a heartfelt, grateful, respectful, affectionate farewell." This was in March of 1870.

Dickens retired to the seclusion of his beautiful country home at Gad's Hill in Kent on the Dover Road. There he set himself to his last, his unfinished, task. He had planned a story to be called *The Mystery of Edwin Drood*, involving the attempted murder of Drood under circumstances of impressive horror— the scene being laid in the crypt and the towers of a cathedral on a wild midnight of wind and storm. Hour after hour, as the long days of early summer drew on, Dickens sat in the little chalet that he had built in his grounds as a workroom, his pen moving rapidly over the paper. For he had no time to lose. It was later than he thought. Beside the doomed man, as he wrote, there stood a shrouded figure waiting to call him away. The summons came. On the evening of June 8, 1870, Dickens left his workroom for his house, where he sat, dazed and ill, trying to write odd letters. As he sat down to dinner his speech failed, his words became muttered and incoherent. "Come and lie down," said his sister-in-law. "Yes," he answered indistinctly, "on the ground."

GAD'S HILL PLACE

With that he fell to the floor. These were his last words. Next morning he was dead. (June 9, 1870.)

The great outburst of national affection which was called forth by Charles Dickens's death led to his burial in Westminster Abbey, in spite of his own expressed wishes against the pomp and ceremony of a public interment. He was buried with great simplicity, but the flowers thrown into the grave till it was filled to the brim bore better witness to the universal sorrow than mere form and pageantry. Nor is there any spot on the flagstoned floor of the great abbey round which even today the passing visitor stands in greater reverence.

The book that Dickens left behind apparently about half finished remains the "mystery" that he called it. We may only conjecture the end, and controversy has never settled whether the unhappy Drood is alive or dead. After Dickens was gone the unfinished papers were found on his study table. The close may be reproduced, not for the story's sake, for by themselves these last pages are not understandable, but for the melancholy interest that attaches to the last words coming to us from one who for a whole generation had delighted and elevated his fellow men.

PIECES AT THE FALL OF THE CURTAIN
Edwin Drood. *The Unfinished Chapter*

(*The closing page of* Edwin Drood, *in which Mr. Datchery—someone in disguise but we do not know who—is seeking for traces of the vanished Drood*):

THE SERVICE [at the cathedral] comes to an end, and the servitors disperse to breakfast. Mr. Datchery accosts his last new acquaintance outside, when the Choir (as much in a hurry to get their bedgowns off, as they were but now to get them on) have scuffled away.

"Well, mistress. Good-morning. You have seen him?"

"*I*'ve seen him, deary: *I*'ve seen him!"

"And you know him?"

"Know him! Better far than all the Reverend Parsons put together know him."

Mrs. Tope's care has spread a very neat, clean breakfast ready for her lodger. Before sitting down to it, he opens his corner-cupboard door; takes his bit of chalk from its shelf; adds one thick line to the score, extending from the top of the cupboard door to the bottom; and then falls to with an appetite.

WHAT MACREADY THE ACTOR THOUGHT OF DICKENS THE READER

(From a letter of Dickens's January, 8, 1862)

WHEN I got home after *Copperfield*, I found him [Macready] quite unable to speak, and able to do nothing but square his dear old jaw all on one side, and roll his eyes (half closed), like Jackson's picture of him. And when I said something light about it, he returned: "No—er—Dickens! I swear to Heaven that, as a piece of passion and playfulness—er—indescribably mixed up together, it does—er—no, really, Dickens!—amaze me as profoundly as it moves me. But as a piece of art— and you know—er—that I—no, Dickens! By—! have seen the best art in a great time—it is incomprehensible to me. How is it got at—er—how is it done—er—how one man can—well? It lays me on my—er—back, and it is of no use talking about it!"

DICKENS'S FAREWELL SPEECH TO AMERICA

(*Delmonico's, New York, April 18, 1870*)

"GENTLEMEN, so much of my voice has lately been heard in the land, and I have, for upwards of four hard winter months, so contended against what I have been sometimes quite admiringly assured was a 'true American catarrh'—a possession which I have throughout highly appreciated, though I might have preferred to be naturalized by any other outward and visible signs —I say, gentlemen, so much of my voice has lately been heard that I might have been contented with troubling you no further from my present standing-point, were it not a duty with which I henceforth charge myself, not only here, but on every suitable occasion, whatsoever and wheresoever, to express my high and grateful sense of my second reception in America, and to bear my honest testimony to the national generosity and magnanimity. Also, to declare how astounded I have been by the amazing changes that I have seen around me on every side, changes moral, changes physical, changes in the amount of land subdued and peopled, changes in the rise of vast new cities, almost out of recognition, changes in the graces and amenities of life, changes in the Press, without whose advancement no advancement can take place anywhere. Nor am I, believe me, so arrogant as to suppose that in the

five-and-twenty years there have been no changes in
me, and that I have nothing to learn and no extreme
impressions to correct when I was here first.

And, gentlemen, this brings me to a point on which
I have, ever since I landed here last November, observed a strict silence, though tempted sometimes to
break it, but in reference to which I will, with your
good leave, take you into my confidence now. Even the
Press, being human, may be sometimes mistaken or
misinformed, and I rather think that I have in one or
two rare instances known its information to be not perfectly accurate with reference to myself. Indeed, I have
now and again been more surprised by printed news
that I have read of myself, than by any printed news
that I have ever read in my present state of existence.
Thus, the vigour and perseverance with which I have
for some months past been collecting materials for,
and hammering away on a new book on America, has
much astounded me, seeing that all that time it has
been perfectly well known to my publishers on both
sides of the Atlantic that I positively declared that no
consideration on earth should induce me to write one.
But what I have intended, what I have resolved upon
(and this is the confidence I seek to place in you) is,
on my return to England, in my own person, to bear,
for the behoof of my countrymen, such testimony to
the gigantic changes in this country as I have hinted
at tonight. Also, to record that wherever I have been,

in the smallest places equally with the largest, I have been received with unsurpassable politeness, delicacy, sweet temper, hospitality, consideration, and with unsurpassable respect for the privacy daily enforced upon me by the nature of my avocation here and the state of my health. This testimony, so long as I live, and so long as my descendants have any legal right in my books, I shall cause to be republished as an appendix to every copy of those two books of mine in which I have referred to America. And this I will do and cause to be done, not in mere love and thankfulness, but because I regard it as an act of plain justice and honour.

*   *   *   *   *

If I know my countrymen, in any and every relation toward America, they begin, not as Sir Anthony Absolute recommended that lovers should begin, with a little aversion, but with a great liking and a profound respect; and whatever little sensitiveness of the moment, or the little official passion, or the little official policy now or then, here or there, may be, take my word for it that the first enduring great popular consideration in England is a generous construction of justice. Finally, gentlemen, and I say this subject to your correction, I do believe from the great majority of honest minds on both sides there cannot be absent the conviction that it would be better for this globe to be ridden by an earthquake, fired by a comet, overrun by an iceberg, and abandoned to the Arctic fox and bear, than that it should present the spectacle of those two great nations, each of whom has, in its own way and hour, striven so hard and successfully for freedom, ever again being arrayed the one against the other.